SCIENCE 1003
Microbiology

LIFEPAC Test is located in the center of the booklet. Please remove before starting the unit.

Author:

Heidi Uilk, M.S.

Editor:

Alan Christopherson, M.S.

MEDIA CREDITS:

Page 5: © Dmitry Knorre, iStock, Thinkstock; **7:** © Jeff Metzger, Hermana, Thinkstock; **8:** © FotoSergio, iStockphoto, Thinkstock; **24:** © Andrey Nekrasov, iStock, Thinkstock; **24:** © Andrew Nekrasor, iStock, Thinkstock; **28:** © Magone, iStock, Thinkstock; © Givaga, iStock, Thinkstock; **29:** © chat9780, iStock, Thinkstock; **39:** © micro_photo, iStock, Thinkstock; **42:** © Comstock Images, Stockbyte, Thinkstock; © ttsz, iStock, Thinkstock; **43:** © ttsz, iStock, Thinkstock; **45:** © DPD CDC; **47:** © Roger De MarfÃ, iStock, Thinkstock; **48:** © Alexander J. da Silva, PhD and Melanie Moser, CDC **57:** © Azot, iStock, Thinkstock, © Spice Walnut; **58:** © ARSUSDA, © micro_photo, iStock, Thinkstock, © Kairi Maileht; **59:** © Shakzu, iStock, Thinkstock, © Guntars Grebezs, iStock, Thinkstock; **60:** © Shane Partridge, iStock, Thinkstock; **61:** © AnnaMariaThor, iStock, Thinkstock; **62:** © Jason Oyadomari; **63:** © Comstock Images, Stockbyte, Thinkstock; **64:** © Mark Brazier, iStock, Thinkstock; **66:** © Daniel Puleo; **67:** © KimOsterhout, iStock, Thinkstock; **73:** © Dr. V.R. Dowel, Jr., CDC; © Dr. David Berd, CDC; **76:** © James Gathany, CDC; **78:** © Alex Gulevich, Dreamstime; **79:** © Matthewe Weinel, Dreamstime, © Pulok Pattanayak, Dreamstime; **80:** © KatarzynaBialasiewicz, iStock, Thinkstock; **81:** © Peshkova, GiStock, Thinkstock, © martynowi_cz, iStock, Thinkstock.

Alpha Omega
PUBLICATIONS

804 N. 2nd Ave. E.
Rock Rapids, IA 51246-1759

Microbiology

Introduction

Biology is the scientific study of God's living creation. There are many, many areas of study that are considered biological studies. In LIFEPAC® 1001, you learned about the science of taxonomy which dealt with classification of living creatures. In LIFEPAC 1002, you studied about molecules, compounds, and chemical reactions as they relate to living organisms, molecular biology. This LIFEPAC will briefly introduce you to **microbiology**, the study of living things too small to be seen without the aide of a microscope. We will also study some larger organisms which are included in the taxonomic kingdoms covered in this LIFEPAC.

The world of microbiology can be described in one word–variety. The differences between the plants and animals we are familiar with seem quite obvious. Green plants carry out photosynthesis. Animals get their energy by ingesting plant material, or by eating animals that ingest plant material.

In the microscopic world, the lines of definition are not quite so clear. Organisms often exhibit characteristics of both plants and animals. For example, the euglena can acquire energy in one of two ways. It can produce its food through photosynthesis, or ingest other organisms. There are also cellular differences that, when examined more closely, reveal great differences between organisms.

God has created an amazing world around us that is teeming with life that we cannot see as we go about our days. Isaiah 45:18 states "For thus saith the Lord that created the heavens; God himself that formed the earth and made it; he hath established it, he created it not in vain, he formed it to be inhabited: I am the Lord; and there is none else."

Objectives

Read these objectives. The objectives tell you what you will be able to do when you have successfully completed this LIFEPAC. Each section will list according to the numbers below what objectives will be met in that section. When you have finished this LIFEPAC, you should be able to:

1. List the kingdoms in the six-kingdom classification system.

2. Identify which kingdoms are composed of prokaryotes and which are made up of eukaryotes.

3. Discuss the history and development of the microscope.

4. List some benefits and limitations of the light microscope and electron microscope.

5. List and describe four phyla of fungi.

6. Discuss what characteristics set organisms of a particular kingdom apart from members of other kingdoms.

7. Discuss the structures and characteristics that allow scientists to place organisms in a particular group such as a phylum within a kingdom.

8. Describe some common forms of reproduction and/or locomotion of the microorganisms studied.

9.   Discuss the economic and environmental impact of the groups of microorganisms.

10. Use proper technique to culture, observe, and identify microorganisms using a light microscope.

11. List and describe six phyla of animal-like protists.

12. List and describe seven phyla of plant-like protists (algae).

13. Discuss the economic and environmental impact of the groups of microorganisms.

14. List and describe three phyla of fungus-like protists.

15. Discuss the economic and environmental impact of some common fungus-like protists.

16. List and describe eubacteria based on Gram staining and shape.

17. List and describe three groups of archaea.

18. List and describe the structures and characteristics of viruses, prions, and viroids.

Survey the LIFEPAC. Ask yourself some questions about this study and write your questions here.

1. MICROBIAL TAXONOMY

In your first LIFEPAC you were introduced to the very important field of biology called taxonomy.

In this section of the Microbiology LIFEPAC, we will briefly revisit this classification process and the six-kingdom taxonomy system as it relates to microscopic organisms.

Section Objectives

Review these objectives. When you have completed this section, you should be able to:

1. List the kingdoms in the six-kingdom classification system.
2. Identify which kingdoms are composed of prokaryotes and which are made up of eukaryotes.
3. Discuss the history and development of the microscope.
4. List some benefits and limitations of the light microscope and electron microscope.

Vocabulary

Study these words to enhance your learning success in this section.

Animalia	Eubacteria	Plantae	prokaryote
Protista	Fungi	Archaea	eukaryote

Note: *All vocabulary words in this LIFEPAC appear in* boldface *print the first time they are used. If you are not sure of the meaning when you are reading, study the definitions given.*

SIX-KINGDOM CLASSIFICATION

The great diversity of these microscopic organisms has for many years caused much discussion (and often disagreement) among taxonomists who attempt to classify these life forms. While we must recognize that there are many taxonomy systems that are being used, the six-kingdom system is one that is commonly accepted and used. In this system, the kingdoms are Animalia (animals), Plantae (plants), Fungi, Protista, Eubacteria, and Archaea. The kingdoms Plantae and Animalia were introduced in your first LIFEPAC. Since the other four kingdoms include mostly microorganisms, we will be studying them in this microbiology LIFEPAC.

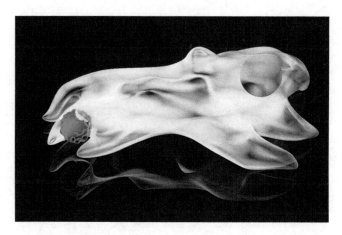

| Phagocytosis

All living organisms can be classified into two groups based on their cellular structure. These two groups are called eukaryotes and prokaryotes. These two groups are based on two very different types of cells. The cellular structure of a prokaryote does not have a true nucleus or any other membrane-bound structures within each cell. The cellular structure of a eukaryote includes a membrane-bound nucleus and various other membrane-bound organelles.

Four of the six kingdoms in the six-kingdom taxonomy system contain organisms classified as eukaryotes. Only two kingdoms, Archaea and Eubacteria, contain all prokaryote. You will study both of these kingdoms in this LIFEPAC. You will also study two kingdoms containing eukaryotes, Fungi and Protista. In a later LIFEPAC you will study the specific structures common to most eukaryotes, while in this LIFEPAC, we will simply be focusing on the structures that are unique to the microorganisms we will be investigating.

CELL TYPE	KINGDOM	GENERAL CHARACTERISTICS	EXAMPLES
Eukaryote	**Animalia**	All multicellular. True tissue and organ differentiation. No cell walls.	Insects, Fish, Birds, Mammals
Eukaryote	**Plantae**	All multicellular. True tissue differentiation. Cell walls composed of cellulose.	Trees, Flowering plants, Grasses, Ferns
Eukaryote	**Fungi**	No tissue differentiation. Cell walls composed of chitin.	Mushrooms, Mold, Yeast
Eukaryote	**Protista**	Cells with true nucleus. Eukaryotes NOT classified as animals, plants, or fungi.	Amoeba, Paramecium, Algae, Slime mold
Prokaryote	**Eubacteria**	Cells have no true nucleus or membrane-bound organelles. Cell walls contain peptidoglycans.	Common bacteria, Blue-green Algae
Prokaryote	**Archaea**	Cells have no true nucleus or membrane-bound organelles. No peptidoglycans in cell walls.	Extremophiles

Complete these activities.

1.1 List the kingdoms that are composed of eukaryotes. a. _____ ,

b. _____ , c. _____ , and d. _____ .

1.2 Which kingdoms are composed of organisms with cell structures which do not have a

membrane-bound nucleus? a. _____ b. _____

1.3 What is the basis for classifying an organism as a prokaryote or a eukaryote?

_____

_____

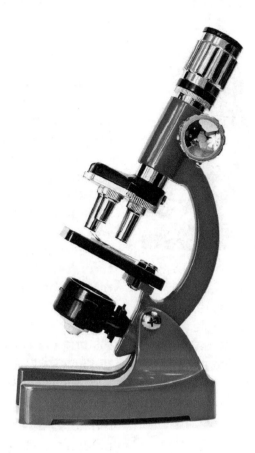

THE MICROSCOPE

The microscope is a tool used by microbiologists to study organisms which are too small to see with the naked eye. These tiny living organisms are commonly referred to as microorganisms. Magnification is required to study microorganisms. Today, magnification is achieved using a wide variety of microscopes. This LIFEPAC section will include a brief history of the microscope as well as techniques necessary for the successful use of microscopes.

Vocabulary

Study these words to enhance your learning success in this section.

microorganisms	dry-mount	scanning electron microscope
monocular	wet-mount	compound microscope
cell	binocular	light (optical) microscope
ocular lens	staining	bright-field microscope
resolving power	objective lens	electron microscope
cover slip	body tube	microscope slide
depression slide		

HISTORY OF THE MICROSCOPE

The development of today's modern microscopes can be traced back well before A.D. 1000 when "burning glasses" were used to focus the sun's rays in order to start a fire. This ability to magnify the sun's rays was accomplished using rock crystals polished to a convex shape. Significant improvements in these basic tools came during the thirteenth century with

| Antique microscope

the invention of spectacles (or eyeglasses). At that time, a single lens that was able to magnify an object to 10 times its actual size was commonly referred to as a "flea glass." As you can imagine, it was often used to view the tiny structures of insects such as fleas. Today, this simple instrument is commonly known as a magnifying glass.

Around 1595, Hans and Zacharias Janssen, Dutch eyeglass makers, experimented with two glass lenses in a tube and found that nearby objects appeared greatly enlarged. The instruments the Janssens' discovered were able to magnify objects to about three to nine times their actual size. In 1609 the Italian physicist and mathematician, Galileo, used mathematics to work out the principles of lenses and made an improved instrument that could be focused. Galileo also took this knowledge about magnification and created one of the first telescopes used extensively in the study of astronomy.

Another Dutchman, Anton van Leeuwenhoek (1632-1723), was one of the earliest and most skillful microscope makers. Leeuwenhoek constructed approximately 400 microscopes during his life, including single-lens microscopes capable of magnification to 270x. Using his microscopes, he was the first to document careful observations and descriptions of blood cells, sperm cells, bacteria, protozoa, and yeasts. Leeuwenhoek described a rainwater drop as having a great multitude of "animalcules."

About the same time that Leeuwenhoek was making his discoveries in Holland, an Englishman, Robert Hooke (1635-1703) was making discoveries of his own, using some of the first microscopes which employed two lenses. These microscopes which use two or more lenses are called compound microscopes. Robert Hooke's most famous discovery using his microscopes was his description of a thin slice of cork. Hooke is credited with first identifying and using the term "cells" to describe the tiny compartments or chambers that made up the cork. Some historians say that the term "cell" is in reference to the small cells or chambers of a beehive. Other historians say that the term "cells" comes from the fact that what Hooke saw reminded him of the small cells of a monastery.

The next notable improvements in microscopes did not come about until the middle of the nineteenth century. At that time, an American, Charles A. Spencer, became known for the extraordinary quality of the microscopes he built. Charles built microscopes that were capable of magnification up to 1250 times using regular light, and up to 5000 times using a blue light source. Spencer was known for creating microscopes with clearer images than anyone had ever seen before. In fact, very little has changed in the design of microscopes since the instruments built by Spencer in the 1840s.

In the 1930s, scientific study of microorganisms changed immensely with the invention of the electron microscope by two Germans, Max Knott and Ernst Ruska. Today, the electron microscope has allowed scientists to view individual molecules that make up the structures in a cell and has changed the science of molecular biology. Molecular biologists study the molecules and reactions of living things and often work closely with microbiologists.

Complete these activities.

1.4 Living creatures which can be seen only by using a microscope are _____ .

1.5 Explain the contribution made to the development of the microscope by each person.

    a. Hans and Zacharias Janssen _____

    _____

    b. Galileo _____

    _____

    c. Anton van Leeuwenhoek _____

    _____

    _____

    d. Robert Hooke _____

    _____

    e. Charles A. Spencer _____

    _____

    _____

    f. Max Knott and Ernst Ruska _____

    _____

1.6 What is a "flea glass"? _____

_____

1.7 What word did Leeuwenhoek use to describe what he saw in a single drop of rainwater?

_____

1.8 What is the significance of Robert Hooke's description of a cork viewed under a microscope?

_____

_____

TYPES OF MICROSCOPES

The modern light (optical) microscope is still one of the most widely used instruments by scientists to magnify microscopic objects for study and experimentation. In this LIFEPAC section we will look at variations of the light microscope.

The invention of the electron microscope has allowed scientists to study individual molecules that are the building blocks of living cells. We will also take a look at two variations of the electron microscope.

The **light (optical) microscope**: A **light microscope** focuses a light source at a specimen through a series of lenses. The light rays which reflect off of the object are then focused into a magnified image. All variations of a light microscope are basically a result of either changing the light source or changing how the light source illuminates the observed specimen.

The most common type of light microscope is the **bright-field microscope**. The bright-field microscope focuses either natural light or incandescent light on a specimen, which produces a magnified image that appears slightly darker on a bright field background. This type is the most frequently used microscope in a classroom by biology students and is the type of microscope you will learn to use in this LIFEPAC.

Other variations of the light microscope have come as a result of the limited ability to produce a clear, magnified image using the full light spectrum. As an image is magnified to higher and higher levels, the image will tend to become less and less sharp. This is because of limited **resolving power**. Resolving power is the ability to distinguish between two points that are very close to each other. You may be familiar with the concept of resolution from shopping for a new television, computer monitor, or digital camera. A digital camera or computer monitor with a high level of resolution produces a very clear image. This is similar to the effect of changing the resolving power. In order to get a clearer view using a light microscope, the resolving power can be increased by either changing the light source or by manipulating the light source to be directed at the specimen in a different way.

The following chart gives you some commonly used variations of the light (optical) microscope.

TYPES OF LIGHT MICROSCOPES	LIGHT SOURCE	COMMON USE
Bright field microscope	Natural light or incandescent bulb. Oil immersion lens may be used to improve resolution.	Most commonly used by biology students.
Dark field microscope	Field of light controlled to create a bright specimen on a dark background.	Improves apparent resolution to see smaller structures in cells. Used to view unstained specimens.
Phase contrast microscope	Takes advantage of the concept that light bends and changes speed as it passes through cell structures.	Makes many structures within a living cell highly visible without staining or altering the cell.
Polarizing light microscope	Limits light wave alignment to vibrate in only one plane.	Used to view molecules or cell structures with highly-ordered patterns.
Fluorescence microscope	Detects the light emitted by fluorescent molecules that are tagged to a specific cell structure. Often uses ultraviolet light.	Used to view very specific cell structures which are prepared using fluorescent molecules.

Rather than focusing light at a specimen, **electron microscopes** utilize streams of electrons which are accelerated in a vacuum and directed at a prepared specimen. The speeding electrons are either absorbed by or bounce off the object at differing angles similar to light waves. The magnified image is then captured on an electron-sensitive plate, similar to photographs being captured on film. Electron microscopes are capable of magnification up to one million times, though the best images are commonly magnified only 250,000 times! These microscopes have been very important in the study of individual molecules, for example the DNA molecules which contain the genetic codes for living organisms.

A common type of electron microscope is called a scanning electron microscope. The scanning electron microscope is capable of producing images that appear to be three-dimensional. This is very helpful for viewing the surface of a cell structure or organic molecule.

While the observations and discoveries made using the electron microscope are indispensable in scientists' study of our Lord God's creation, there are some major drawbacks to the use of an electron microscope. First, an electron microscope is very expensive compared to even the very best light (optical) microscopes. Second, the process of preparing a specimen to be viewed using an electron microscope is quite extensive and time consuming. Third, it is not possible to view a living organism using an electron microscope, because no living being can survive the vacuum it must be placed in for viewing. This makes it impossible to watch the ever-changing movement of a living cell using these powerful instruments.

 Complete these activities.

1.9 Describe how a light microscope creates a magnified image. _____

_____

1.10 What is different about your description in problem 1.9 for an electron microscope?

_____

_____

1.11 What limits the amount of magnification that can be produced using light? Why?

_____

_____

1.12 Name three variations of the light microscope and a common use for each.

a. _____

b. _____

c. _____

1.13 At what level of magnification are the best images produced using an electron microscope?

_____

1.14 Name three limitations to using an electron microscope to view a microorganism.

a. _____

b. _____

c. _____

MICROSCOPE ANATOMY

You learned earlier in this LIFEPAC that a compound microscope uses two or more lenses to create a magnified image. In this section, you will be learning about the parts of a compound microscope and how they are involved in producing a magnified image. In the next LIFEPAC section, you will learn the proper techniques necessary for using a compound microscope to study living and non-living specimens. It may be very helpful for you to get your microscope out and have it available as you continue through this section.

Compound microscopes can be divided into two categories based on the number of tubes used for viewing. A monocular microscope has a single body tube, thus only one eyepiece for looking through. A binocular microscope has two body tubes, and thus two eyepieces used for viewing. The microscope you are using for this class may be either monocular or binocular; however, the parts and basic functions of those parts will be the same in either case.

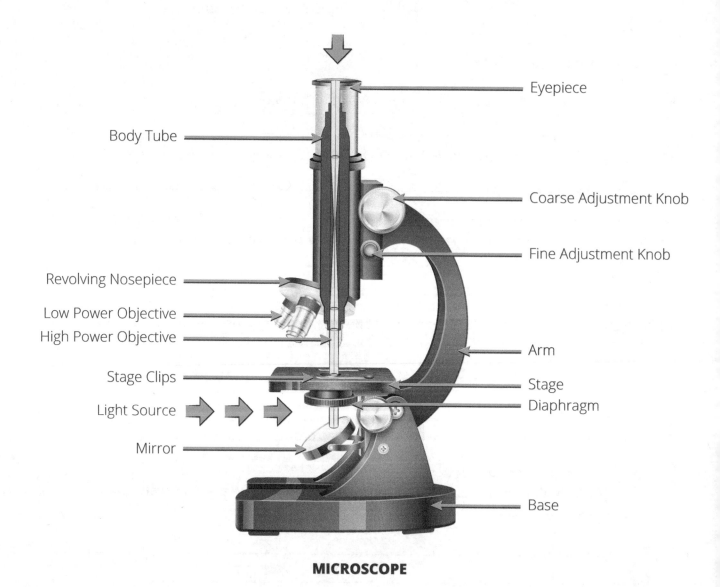

MICROSCOPE

Using the microscope and the following list of questions, take some time to identify the parts of your microscope.

- Is your microscope monocular or binocular? _____

- What does the *high power* objective lens on your microscope say? _____

- What does the *low power* objective lens on your microscope say? _____

- Does your microscope use a natural light source directed by a mirror _____ ;

  or does you microscope have a built-in light source (a light bulb)? _____

- When you turn the adjustment knob, does your *body tube* move up and down or does your

  stage move up and down? _____

As you identify each piece of your microscope, refer to the following table to learn more about each part and how to use it correctly.

PARTS OF MICROSCOPE	DESCRIPTION
Arm	Supports the body tube of the microscope. Always carry a microscope by grasping the arm with one hand and the base with the other hand.
Base	Supports the entire microscope on a flat, level surface. The arm may be solidly attached to the base; or the arm and base may be attached by a movable hinge that would allow a user to tilt the microscope.
Body Tube(s)	Solid structure that connects the eyepiece to the objective lenses. Light passes through the body tube to the eyepiece.
Eyepiece(s)	Part of the microscope you look through to view an object. The eyepiece contains the ocular lens, one of the two lenses in a compound micro-scope. Most ocular lenses produce a magnification of 10x or 15x.
Revolving Nosepiece	Holds the objective lenses on a plate that can be rotated to change the magnification. An objective lens is the lower of two lenses in a com-pound microscope. Be sure that the nosepiece clicks into place to ensure that you will be able to see through the microscope.
Low Power Objective	Usually has a magnification of 10x. Used to scan a slide for the specimen. May also be used to view small external structures, such as the hairs on the legs of a fly.
High Power Objective	Usually has a magnification of 30x, 35x, or 40x. Can be used to identify and study the nucleus and organelles within many eukaryotic cells.

PARTS OF MICROSCOPE	DESCRIPTION
Coarse Adjustment Knob	Either moves the body tube or the stage up and down to bring the object into view. Use the coarse adjustment knob ONLY with the low power objective. CAUTION: Never use the coarse adjustment knob when viewing an object with the high power objective.
Fine Adjustment Knob	Used to bring objects into clear, sharp focus. Use this knob when focusing with the high power objective. If the object has been properly focused using the coarse adjustment knob, then only a tiny movement of the fine adjustment knob should be necessary to bring the object into sharp focus.
Stage	Supports the slide with the specimen that is being viewed. In the center of the stage is a hole that allows light to pass through from below the stage.
Stage Clips	Hold the slide in place on the stage. Gently move the clips out of the way to place the slide into place, and then gently move the clips back into place on the edges of the slide. CAUTION: Never allow the clips to come into contact with the opening in the stage. They will easily scratch the glass covering the opening.
Diaphragm	A rotating plate located just below the stage with holes of various sizes. Rotating the diaphragm allows you to increase or decrease the amount of light that is allowed to enter the microscope.
Mirror or Light Source	Used to collect light and direct it into the microscope. CAUTION: Never use direct sunlight as a source of light. Sunlight directed off the mirror can damage your eyes. Your microscope may include a built-in light source in the form of an electric light bulb. In that case, there will be no mirror.

Calculation of magnification. So far, you have seen the strength of the ocular and objective lenses referred to as 10x, 15x, 40x, etc. But how do you calculate the total magnification of the image? As you may have assumed, "10x" means that particular lens magnifies an image to ten times its actual size. The total amount of magnification of your microscope is calculated by multiplying the powers of the ocular lens and objective lens. If the magnification of your microscopes ocular lens it 10x and the high power objective is 45x, then your total magnification on high power is 10 x 45 = 450x.

Complete these activities.

1.15 When using a _____ microscope, you would look through two eyepieces.

1.16 What part of a microscope rotates to change from the low power objective lens to the high

power objective lens? _____

1.17 When are you never supposed to use the coarse adjustment knob? .

_____

1.18 Which lens is closest to your eye when looking through a microscope? _____

1.19 Which lens is closest to the object that you are viewing? _____

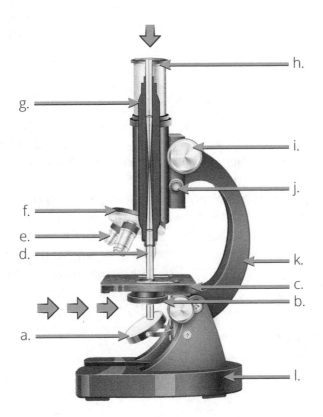

Fill in the blanks.

1.20 Label the diagram of the microscope.

a. _____   b. _____   c. _____

d. _____   e. _____   f. _____

g. _____   h. _____   i. _____

j. _____   k. _____   l. _____

1.21 Complete the following table by calculating the total magnification.

Ocular Lens	Objective Lens	Total Magnification
10x	20x	a.
10x	45x	b.
10x	40x	c.
15x	20x	d.
15x	40x	e.

TECHNIQUES OF MICROSCOPY

Sample preparation. Objects that are going to be viewed using a microscope must be prepared in such a way as to maximize the usefulness of the microscope. Since the magnified image of the specimen is produced by passing light through the object, it makes sense that the object must be thin enough to allow sufficient light to pass through.

Most specimens being viewed using a light microscope are prepared on a glass micro-scope slide. These preparations are either a wet-mount or dry-mount. A dry-mount preparation simply means that the object being viewed is placed on the microscope slide and viewed as it is. A wet-mount preparation means that the specimen is immersed in water or another liquid. In both cases, a cover slip is placed over the specimen to create a barrier between the specimen and the end of the objective lens. Later in this LIFEPAC, you will be instructed to use a depression slide to prepare a specimen. A depression slide has a small well (or depression) in it to allow for a slightly larger volume of water to be held on the microscope slide.

Another common part of preparing a specimen to be viewed under a microscope involves staining the cell structures we are interested in viewing. For example, a scientist may add a stain called methylene blue to a cell. Since the methylene blue stain will stain only the DNA and RNA in a cell, it can be used to see the contents of the cell nucleus more clearly. Other means of marking special structures in a cell may include using any of a great variety of other dyes (stains), fluorescent dyes, or even radioactive makers.

View Two 1003 Clips: Ranch Adventure and How to Use a Microscope, from the 10th Grade SCIENCE EXPERIMENTS Video

LEARNING APPLICATION: Using the microscope.

In the following activity, you will learn how to prepare a wet-mount slide and observe that slide using the microscope.

These supplies are needed:

- compound microscope
- microscope slide
- cover slip
- pin

- newspaper
- medicine dropper
- water
- scissors

Follow these directions. Put a check mark in the box when each step is completed.

☐ 1. Cut a small letter "g" from the newspaper and place it in the center of the glass microscope slide. For this experiment, try to center the letter "g," keep the letter upright, and keep the bottom of the letter parallel to the bottom of your microscope slide. This will make the sketches asked for later simpler. (Newspaper works best for this activity since the paper is fairly thin, this allows enough light to pass through it for viewing with a microscope.)

☐ 2. To make a wet-mount slide, place a small drop of water directly on the specimen (letter "g") using a medicine dropper.

☐ 3. Cover the specimen with a clean cover slip. To do this properly, place one edge of the cover slip at the edge of the drop of water while holding the cover slip at a 45 degree angle to the microscope slide. Using a pin to hold the cover slip, slowly lower the cover slip over the specimen and the drop of water. The goal is to make sure you do not capture any air bubbles under the cover slip.

☐ 4. On the diagram below, draw a picture of the prepared wet-mount slide as you see it sitting on the table in front of you. Do your best to create your drawing to scale.

☐ 5. Clip the wet-mount slide into place on the stage of the microscope. Place the letter "g" directly over the center of the hole on the microscope stage.

(Continued on next page)

☐ 6. Look at the microscope stage from the side. DO NOT look through the eyepiece yet. Turn the revolving nosepiece to place the low power objective over your specimen. Using the course adjustment knob, lower the tube body (or raise the stage) until the low power objective ALMOST touches the microscope slide.

☐ 7. Looking through the eyepiece, slowly raise the body tube (or lower the stage) until the letter "g" comes into clear view.

☐ 8. Using the fine adjustment knob, while turning no more than a ¼ turn, focus the specimen as clearly as possible. At this point, you may need to adjust your light source to maximize the clarity of your image.

☐ 9. In the circle provided, sketch the letter "g" as it appears through the microscope. Note the low power magnification:

_____

☐ 10. While looking through the eyepiece, carefully move the slide to the left. Which way does the letter move?

_____

Now move the slide to the right. Which way does the letter move?

_____

After re-centering the slide, move the slide toward yourself. Which way does the letter move?

_____

☐ 11. To switch to the high power objective: Look at the microscope from the side, (DO NOT look through the eyepiece) then rotate the revolving nosepiece so that high power objective clicks into place. Using the fine adjustment knob ONLY, carefully bring the specimen into focus.

CAUTION: *If you are unable to bring the specimen into focus with a ¼ turn of the fine adjustment knob then STOP! NEVER use the course adjustment knob while viewing using high power. Since high power objectives are longer than low power objectives, by using the coarse adjustment knob you risk forcing the high power objective lens into your slide; thus damaging both the objective lens and your specimen.*

Instead, turn back to the low power objective; while viewing with the low power objective, follow proper technique as outlined above to refocus using the coarse adjustment knob and the fine adjustment knob. Then, turn back to the high power objective and use slight movements of the fine adjustment knob to refocus.

☐ 12. In the circle provided, sketch the letter "g" as it appears through the microscope. (Depending on the power of your microscope, you may only see a very small part of the letter.)

Describe what details you can now see on high power that you could not see on low power.

_____

_____

_____

_____

_____

Record the high power magnification:

_____

☐ 13. OPTIONAL ACTIVITY: Obtain two more specimens to be viewed under the microscope. Some ideas may be: a piece of colored thread, a piece of your hair, dirt from under your fingernail, the wing of a dead fly, etc. Prepare wet-mount slides of each specimen, and then follow proper procedure to view each one, using low power and high power objectives. In the space provided, names your items, sketch them at low and high power, and discuss what you see with the microscope compared to what you can see with your naked eyes.

Specimen #1: _____

_____

_____

_____

_____

_____

_____

Low Power: _____

High Power: _____

Specimen #2: _____

_____

_____

_____

_____

_____

_____

Low Power: _____

High Power: _____

TEACHER CHECK _____ _____

initials   date

Complete the following activities.

1.22 Why are stains used when observing a specimen under a microscope? _____

_____

1.23 Describe how to prepare a wet-mount slide. _____

_____

_____

1.24 What could happen if you used the coarse adjustment knob while viewing a specimen with the high power objective? _____

_____

_____

Review the material in this section in preparation for the Self Test. The Self Test will check your mastery of this particular section. The items missed on this Self Test will indicate specific areas where restudy is needed for mastery.

SELF TEST 1

Complete these activities (each answer, 6 points).

1.01 Name the two kingdoms where all prokaryotes are classified. _____

_____

1.02 List the four kingdoms where all eukaryotes are classified. _____

_____

1.03 Explain what safety measures you might take to avoid damaging the microscope, microscope slide, or a living specimen on you microscope stage.

_____

_____

_____

_____

_____

_____

1.04 Explain three disadvantages to using an electron microscope to view microorganisms.

_____

_____

_____

Match these items (each answer, 3 points).

1.05 _____ resolving power

1.06 _____ objective lens

1.07 _____ optical microscope

1.08 _____ monocular

1.09 _____ electron microscope

1.010 _____ prokaryote

1.011 _____ binocular

1.012 _____ ocular lens

1.013 _____ eukaryote

a. cell with no membrane-bound structures

b. ability to tell two points apart

c. magnifies an object using light and lenses

d. magnifies using streams of electrons

e. single body tube

f. cell with a true nucleus

g. lens found in the eyepiece

h. two eyepieces

i. magnifying lens closest to the specimen

Complete these statements (each answer, 4 points).

1.014 As a predecessor to today's microscopes, a _____ was used to focus the sun's light in order to start a fire.

1.015 The Englishman who first used the term "cells" to describe tiny compartments which made up cork was _____ .

1.016 Galileo used _____ to examine the principles of lenses, thus improving on previous attempts at magnification.

1.017 The Dutchman, _____ , was the first to carefully document observations of blood cells, sperms cells, and other microorganisms.

1.018 _____ and _____ , two sixteenth century eyeglass makers, experimented with glass lenses and a tube and found that objects could be magnified greatly.

1.019 Very little has changed in the structure of light microscopes since the 1840s when an American, _____ , was able to significantly improve the quality of the magnified images with his microscopes.

1.020 The electron microscope was invented in Germany by _____ and _____ during the 1930s.

Number the following items (1, 2, 3, 4, 5) **in order from your eye to the specimen on the stage of your microscope** (each answer, 2 points).

1.021 _____ objective lens

1.022 _____ body tube

1.023 _____ ocular lens

1.024 _____ cover slip

1.025 _____ revolving nosepiece

2. FUNGI

You have learned about light and electron microscopes; undoubtedly, these are some of the most useful tools we have available to learn about God's microscopic creation. Throughout the rest of this LIFEPAC, you will be asked to use the microscope techniques you have just learned to study various microorganisms in the kingdoms Fungi, Protista, Eubacteria, and Archaea. You will also read about viruses and the diseases associated with them.

In this section, you will be studying the microscopic and multicellular organisms that are included in the four phyla within the kingdom Fungi. As you may remember from a previous LIFEPAC, a phylum is the next level of division under kingdom used to group organisms based on similar characteristics. All organisms classified within the kingdom Fungi are assigned to one of the four phyla: Basidiomycota, Ascomycota, Zygomycota, or Chytridiomycota.

Section Objectives

Review these objectives. When you have completed this section, you should be able to:

5. List and describe four phyla of fungi.

6. Discuss what characteristics set organisms of a particular kingdom apart from members of other kingdoms.

7. Discuss the structures and characteristics that allow scientists to place organisms in a particular group such as a phylum within a kingdom.

8. Describe some common forms of reproduction and/or locomotion of the microorganisms studied.

9. Discuss the economic and environmental impact of the groups of microorganisms.

10. Use proper technique to culture, observe, and identify microorganisms using a light microscope.

Vocabulary

Study these words to enhance your learning success in this section.

phylum	mycelia	morels	zygosporangium
chitin	rhizoids	club fungi	zygospore
host	gills	penicillin	sporangiophore
spores	ascus	budding	saprophytes
parasite	ring	sporangium	Zygomycota
symbiosis	sac fungi	Basidiomycota	Chytridiomycota
lichens	stalk	fermentation	multi-nucleated
cap	hyphae	Ascomycota	fruiting bodies
stolon			

KINGDOM FUNGI

Before we take a look at some members of each individual phylum, let's take a look at some common characteristics of the approximately 100,000 species in the kingdom Fungi. In years past, fungi were classified as part of the kingdom Plantae. Fungi are now classified as their own kingdom based on a number of characteristics. Three characteristics that make fungus different from plants are: they do not produce their own food using chlorophyll, there is no tissue differentiation such as leaf material and root material, and the cell walls of fungi are composed of a material called chitin. Plant cell walls are composed of cellulose. Chitin, on the other hand, is a material found in the exoskeleton of some animals and insects!

Almost all fungi can be classified as either parasites or saprophytes. Parasites live directly on other living organisms, often to the detriment of the host organism, such as in the case of Dutch elm disease which has killed millions of elm trees all across America since the 1930s. A host organism is a plant or animal that supports a parasite. Saprophytes, on the other hand, obtain all their food from non-living plant and animal material and are very important parts of the decaying/recycling process God has put into motion to "clean up" in nature.

There are some fungi that share a positive relationship with another organism. This relationship, which is essentially a "win-win" situation for the fungus and another living organism, is called symbiosis. Lichens are an example of fungi and an alga or cyanobacteria depending on each other to live in a particular environment. In most cases, neither the fungi nor the alga would be able to survive in a particular environment without the other.

Most fungi are multicellular organisms (except yeast) and contain cells which are multi-nucleated, meaning that there is more than one nucleus inside some individual cells. Multicellular fungi have thread-like structures called hyphae. Hyphae grouped together form all of the different structures of fungi. A group of hyphae which form a visible structure and performing a specific function is called mycelia.

Some hyphae group together to form structures called rhizoids that are responsible for obtaining food for the organism. These structures produce an enzyme which is responsible for breaking down organic material into smaller molecules. These smaller molecules can be absorbed by the fungus directly through its cell membrane to be used as a food source.

Other mycelia form the structures responsible for reproduction. These reproductive structures are referred to as fruiting bodies. Fungi are classified into phyla based on their means of reproduction and the structure of their fruiting bodies. Fungi are capable of both sexual and asexual reproduction, depending on the environmental conditions. Spores are small reproductive cells, often with some protective covering, which are dispersed from the fruiting body. A new, complete fungus can grow from a single spore if it lands in favorable conditions for growth.

Another general grouping of fungi is based on the shape of the actual structures which produce the spores. A group commonly called club fungi is so called because of the club shape of the spore-producing structure. Fungi which produce spores inside a sac-like structure are generally called sac fungi.

| Mushrooms

Complete these activities.

2.1 Give three reasons that fungi are no longer classified as plants.

a. _____

b. _____

c. _____

2.2 Define each term.

a. symbiosis _____

b. parasite _____

_____

c. saprophyte _____

_____

2.3 Multicellular fungi are composed of thread-like structures called _____ which group together to form _____ to perform specific functions.

2.4 Explain how rhizoids function to obtain food for a fungus. _____

_____

_____

2.5 In fungus, the reproductive structures are called _____ . From these structures, _____ are released from which a complete fungus can grow.

2.6 The common grouping of fungi into the club fungi group or the sac fungi group are based on what characteristic? _____

2.7 Name the four phyla of fungi you will be studying in this section.

a. _____   b. _____

c. _____   d. _____

LEARNING APPLICATION Part 1: Fungus all around.

In the following activity, you will grow and observe a number of different samples of fungus which are all around you in your home. You will need to start this activity today, then come back to complete it after two or three days have passed.

These supplies are needed:

- slice of hard cheese
- slice of bread
- orange, apple, or banana peel
- 3 sealable plastic sandwich bags

Follow these directions. Put a check mark in the box when each step is completed.

Sample preparation:

☐ 1. Inoculate your growing media; slice of cheese, slice of bread, and fruit peel. Gently wipe each media across a dusty surface. You may need to gently flatten a piece of your fruit peeling to make sure a large surface area comes in contact with the dust.

☐ 2. Place each inoculated item in a separate sealable plastic sandwich bag. Add 2 tablespoons of water to each bag and then seal the bags.

☐ 3. Place all three bags in a dark, warm location for four or five days or however long it takes to see mold growing on each item.

PHYLA OF FUNGI

PHYLUM BASIDIOMYCOTA (COMMON MUSHROOMS)

Basidiomycota include common organisms such as mushrooms, toadstools, puffballs, bracket fungi, rusts, and smuts. We will discuss the most common representative of this phylum, the mushroom. You will not need a microscope to see a mushroom; however, some magnification is quite helpful for viewing some of the tiny structures of a mushroom.

The most conspicuous structure of a mushroom is the cap. The cap is the umbrella-shaped top of a mushroom and is the mushroom's fruiting body. The underside of the cap contains structures called gills. The gills are the structures where reproductive spores are produced and released. Because of the shape of the spore-producing structures, mushrooms are grouped as club fungi. The mushroom cap

and gills are supported by a stem-like structure called a stalk. Found on the stalk, another structure referred to as the ring can be

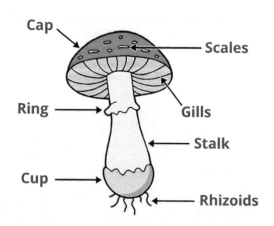

| Diagram of a mushroom

identified. The **ring** is a structure left over from a protective covering that was present when the mushroom was first developing. The part of the mushroom that you can't see without magnification is the hyphae (rhizoids) which grow into the organic material the mushroom depends on as its food source.

Most of us are familiar with mushrooms as a human food source. In fact, mushroom farming is a very big industry; in 2014-2015, mushroom farmers in the United States produced 953 million pounds of mushrooms! Didn't you ever wonder where all those mushrooms on your pizza came from? The most common kind of edible mushroom is *Agaricus bisporis*. These are the white mushrooms you can find in most grocery stores.

Of course, it would be best to note that not all mushrooms are edible. In fact, one type of mushroom is properly named a "death cap" mushroom. This mushroom produces a protein molecule which kills the human liver and kidneys. If this mushroom is mistakenly eaten, death will occur within five days if a liver and kidney transplant is not immediately available.

Caution: *Do not pick and eat wild mushrooms.*

 Complete these activities.

2.8 List at least four common organisms that are part of the phylum Basidiomycota.

_____

2.9 Which structure of the mushroom do we typically recognize them by? _____

2.10 Give a brief description of each structure of a mushroom.

    a. cap _____

    b. gills _____

    c. stalk _____

    d. ring _____

    e. rhizoids _____

2.11 What is the scientific name of the most common mushroom you find in the grocery store?

_____

PHYLUM ASCOMYCOTA

The phylum Ascomycota comprises well over half of all species of fungi with more than 30,000 known species. Yeast and **morels** are two common names of organisms which fit within this category. Yeasts are unicellular and morels are multicellular. Because of the sac-like shape of their fruiting bodies, called **ascus**, they are classified as sac fungi.

Morels are also called sponge mushrooms, though they are not truly mushrooms at all. From the previous section, you learned that mushrooms are designated as club fungi. Morels, on the other hand, are classified as sac fungi and do not share the many structures in common with basidiomycetes (mushrooms).

| Bread dough

| Cheese

We will not spend a lot of time here reviewing the structure of morels; however, you can find plenty of information on the Internet about identifying morels, since they are commonly collected from forest floors each spring by avid "mushroom hunters" as a favorite delicacy and an exciting challenge!

Yeasts are quite different from most other fungi. They are the only fungi that are unicellular, although there are a few species that may form tiny multicellular structures during a portion of their life cycle. Another way that yeasts differ is in their ability to reproduce asexually through a process called budding. Budding is the production of a new organism by pinching off a portion of a parent cell. Yeasts are similar to many other fungi because they are also able to reproduce sexually. As we mentioned earlier, yeasts are commonly included as a member of the sac fungi. Since yeasts are unicellular, the entire cell becomes the ascus.

Like other fungi, yeasts obtain their food from external sources by a process called fermentation. This is the process of breaking down complex molecules into simpler molecules that can be used by cells as food. One of the products produced during fermentation is carbon dioxide gas. This by-product of yeasts is what makes *Saccharomyces cerevisiae*, or baker's yeast, very important in the baking industry. Carbon dioxide gas released by the yeast is what makes bread rise. Yeasts are also important for many other reasons, including as flavoring for cheeses such as Camembert, Roquefort (Bleu Cheese), and Brie. Other yeasts, such as Ceratocystis ulmi are responsible for the wide-spread destruction of elm trees by Dutch elm disease in the United States. Like other fungi, yeasts are also important decomposers in nature.

One of the most well-known fungi, *Penicillium chrysogenum*, is typically classified as an asco-mycete. (There is some uncertainty about where it should be classified.) Sir Alexander Fleming is credited for first discovering and documenting the antibiotic effects of a colony of blue-green mold in 1928. Penicillin, once isolated and produced on a larger scale, changed the world of medicine in ways no other discovery since then has rivaled.

Complete these activities.

2.12 List two common organisms which are part of the phylum Ascomycota.

_____   _____

2.13 The _____ is the name of the fruiting body for all sac fungi.

2.14 Where are morels commonly found growing? _____

2.15 Define the following processes.

    a. budding _____

    b. fermentation _____

2.16 Explain the importance of the following species of yeast.

    a. Saccharomyces cerevisiae _____

    b. Ceratocystis ulmi _____

    c. Penicillium chrysogenum _____

PHYLUM ZYGOMYCOTA (COMMON MOLD)

Have you ever retrieved a loaf of bread and a jar of jelly from your kitchen to make your favorite sandwich, only to find that the bread and jelly were both covered in green, white, or black fuzz? If so, you are already familiar with zygomycetes. The mold on your bread is one of less than 1,000 known species included in the phylum Zygomycota. Almost all members of this group are terrestrial saprophytes which feed on decaying plant and animal material. The spores of these common molds are most often associated with seasonal hay fever and allergies for humans.

The name of this phylum comes from a reproductive structure which forms when the hyphae of two zygomycetes of the same species come in contact. This structure is called a zygosporangium and is where sexual reproduction occurs. The new mold which grows from the zygospore contains genetic material from each of the organisms which came into contact.

Remember from our initial discussion about fungi, that the different structures of a fungus are made up of masses of hyphae. When you are looking at bread mold without magnification, it is very hard, if not impossible, to see the individual structures. With the help of a strong magnifying glass or a light microscope, it is possible to identify the structures formed by the hyphae of common mold.

When a single spore lands in a place with favorable growing conditions, then it will quickly grow a colony by asexual reproduction. Rhizoids will form to begin the process of external digestion on the surface the mold is growing on. Tiny stalk-like structures of mycelia called sporangiophore grow to support the sporangium, where the spores are produced and released. Long hyphae called stolon, make up the white "fuzz" you see on a moldy surface. Stolons act as the anchors for the mold and connect one sporangiophore to another.

| Bread mold growing in ripe fruit cell

PHYLUM CHYTRIDIOMYCOTA

Chytridiomycota, commonly referred to as chytrids, are quite different than the other three phyla of fungi for two main reasons. First, most of the approximately 1,000 members of this group are aquatic, which means they live in water, while almost all other fungi live on land. Second, the gametes or reproductive cells are flagellated, which means that they have a tail-like structure that allows them to propel themselves through the water. (You will learn more about flagella during your study of the kingdom Protista.) These two reasons cause biologists and taxonomists to disagree that these organisms should be included in the kingdom Fungi. Many argue that these organisms fit better in the kingdom Protista.

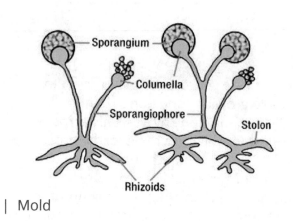

| Mold

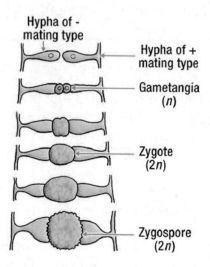

| Zygospore formation

Complete these activities.

2.17 Most species in the kingdom Zygomycota are _____

which feed on decaying plant and animal material.

2.18 Briefly describe the sexual reproduction cycle for zygomycetes. _____

_____

_____

2.19 Give a short description of each structure of a mold.

a. sporangiophore _____

b. sporangium _____

c. stolon _____

2.20 Give two reasons that chytrids differ significantly from other fungi. _____

_____

View Two 1003 Clips: Microscope: Fungi and Camembert Cheese, from the 10th Grade SCIENCE EXPERIMENTS Video

LEARNING APPLICATION
Part 2: Fungus all around.

These supplies are needed:

- compound microscope
- depression slide
- cover slip
- methylene blue stain
- sugar
- baker's yeast packet
- 5x or 10x hand lens
- tweezers

- cup or glass
- fresh whole mushroom
- medicine dropper
- sharp knife or razor blade
- flashlight
- pin
- spoon

Follow these directions. Put a check mark in the box when each step is completed.

Yeast observation:

☐ 1. In a glass, mix the contents of the baker's yeast packet, a tablespoon of sugar, and two cups of warm (not hot) water.

☐ 2. Allow the mixture to sit for approximately ten minutes. You are waiting for the yeast cells to begin to grow and multiply.

☐ 3. Using the medicine dropper, place a drop of the yeast mixture into the well of a depression slide. Add one drop of methylene blue stain.

☐ 4. Place a cover slip over the sample. You may now carefully place your prepared slide on the microscope stage for viewing.

☐ 5. Focus the slide on low power. You may then switch the objective to high power and refocus with tiny movements of the fine adjustment knob. In the space provided, sketch and label what you see. Be sure to identify a reproducing yeast cell and the tiny bubbles of carbon dioxide given off by the cells. How does yeast reproduce?

_____

Record the magnification of the high

power objective: _____

(Continued on next page)

Mushroom observation:

☐ 6. Obtain a fresh whole mushroom and a hand lens. Do you know what kind of mushroom you are looking at? _____ If so, what is the scientific name? (Example: Agaricus bisporis)

_____

In the space provided, sketch and label your mushroom sample. Be sure to label all structures you are able to identify.

Mold observation:

☐ 7. Remove each of your mold samples from their plastic bags. Using your 5x or 10x magnifying lens and your nose, make a detailed sketch and description of each sample. Include a **detailed description** of the mold colonies present on each sample. For each sample, be sure your discussion includes detailed descriptions of each kind of colony (size, color(s), smell, depth, total number on sample, etc.). Each sample may include more than one kind of mold, so be sure to provide a separate detailed description of each one. You may need to attach a separate piece of paper for your detailed descriptions.

Cheese sample:

_____

_____

_____

_____

_____

_____

Fruit peel sample:

_____

_____

_____

_____

_____

_____

Bread sample:

_____

_____

_____

_____

_____

_____

☐ 8. Choose three different colonies to observe using your microscope. The three colonies do not have to come from each media. For example, if you have three different kinds of colonies growing on the bread, all three specimens can be taken from the bread. You will not be using the high power magnification on you microscope for this experiment. In order to maintain the delicate structures of the colonies, you will not be using a cover slip over your sample.

Important: *Extra special care must be taken to make sure the objective lens never comes in contact with the specimen since it is not covered.*

☐ 9. To prepare your sample, using your sharp knife, razor blade, and/or pin, cut away an entire colony from the media. Very carefully, lift the colony from the very edge, using your tweezers. Place the colony on the center of a microscope slide.

☐ 10. Your colony will be a few millimeters thick and may be wider than the field of view on your lowest objective setting on your microscope; thus the light source below the stage of your microscope will not be sufficient. You will need to use your flashlight to provide a light source from the side of the specimen.

☐ 11. Using proper technique, focus your scanning or lowest power objective on your colony.

Important: *Extra special care must be taken to make sure the objective lens never comes in contact with the specimen since it is not covered.*

☐ 12. If you have started with a scanning objective lens, then change to low power objective. ****Maximum for this experiment should be 100x**** You should be able to refocus simply by making minimal movement of the fine adjustment knob. Draw and label what you see on the next page.

Magnification: _____

1st Colony: Describe what you see.
What specific structures can you identify?

_____

_____

_____

_____

_____

_____

2nd Colony: Describe what you see.
What specific structures can you identify?

_____

_____

_____

_____

_____

_____

3rd Colony: Describe what you see.
What specific structures can you identify?

_____

_____

_____

_____

_____

_____

TEACHER CHECK _____ _____
                      initials   date

Review the material in this section in preparation for the Self Test. This Self Test will check your mastery of this particular section as well as your knowledge of the previous section.

SELF TEST 2

Answer true or false (each answer, 2 points).

2.01 _____ The cell wall of fungi is composed of chitin, the same material found in the exoskeleton of a lobster.

2.02 _____ Ascomycota is an example of a kingdom.

2.03 _____ An electron microscope is necessary to view yeast cells budding.

2.04 _____ Fungi are commonly grouped as sac fungi or club fungi based on the structure of their fruiting bodies.

2.05 _____ Fungi are prokaryotes.

2.06 _____ The limiting characteristic of an electron microscope is often the resolving power.

2.07 _____ Max Knott and Ernst Ruska invented the electron microscope.

2.08 _____ A zygospore is the product of sexual reproduction.

2.09 _____ The fuzzy-looking structures in a mold colony are called sporangium.

Match these items (each answer, 3 points).

2.010 _____ taxonomic category within a kingdom

2.011 _____ obtain food from non-living organic material

2.012 _____ break down of complex molecules into simpler ones

2.013 _____ multi-nucleated thread-like structures of fungi

2.014 _____ mycelia responsible for obtaining food

2.015 _____ asexual reproduction of yeast

2.016 _____ a group of hyphae

2.017 _____ reproductive cells which can tolerate bad conditions

2.018 _____ structures which house the reproductive formation

2.019 _____ mutually positive relationship between two species

2.020 _____ plant or animal which supports a parasite

a. mycelia

b. phylum

c. saprophyte

d. symbiosis

e. fermentation

f. rhizoids

g. hyphae

h. budding

i. spores

j. host

k. fruiting bodies

Match the scientific name with the description (each answer, 3 points).

2.021 _____ common edible mushroom

2.022 _____ produces common antibiotic

2.023 _____ baker's yeast

2.024 _____ elm tree parasite

a. Ceratocystis ulmi

b. Saccharomyces cerevisiae

c. Penicillium chrysogenum

d. Agaricus bisporis

Complete these activities (each numbered item, 3 points).

2.025 Give two reasons members of the phylum Chytridiomycota are sometimes grouped in the kingdom Protista rather than the kingdom Fungi.

a. _____

b. _____

2.026 Who is credited with discovering penicillin? _____

2.027 _____ used mathematics to examine the principles of lenses, thus improving on previous attempts at magnification.

2.028 What name did Robert Hooke give to the compartments in a cork sample that he observed using a microscope? _____

Fill in the blanks (each numbered item, 3 points).

2.029 Label the diagram of a mushroom.

a. _____

b. _____

c. _____

d. _____

e. _____

f. _____

g. _____

SCORE_____   TEACHER_____ _____

79 / 99

initials   date

3. ANIMAL-LIKE PROTISTS

KINGDOM PROTISTA

The species which make up the kingdom Protista are undoubtedly the most diverse of all organisms in the six-kingdom taxonomic system. This is the final kingdom we will study that is made up of eukaryotic organisms. Beyond this common cell structure, there are not many characteristics in common between the species in the phyla of kingdom Protista. In fact, a eukaryotic organism that is NOT animal, NOT plant, and NOT fungus is called a protist.

With the use of the electron microscope, research continues on the molecular structures of these organisms. Because of this research, the taxonomic phyla continue to change rapidly. Two organisms that may have long been considered very similar to each other because of the way they look under a light microscope may be re-classified when it is learned that their cell wall is made of completely different organic compounds. Even as this text is being written, there are scientists that will debate (rightfully so) the validity of any taxonomic structure used. While we will not take an in-depth look at all the phyla of the kingdom Protista, we will briefly discuss a wide cross-section of representative organisms.

Organisms are classified within the kingdom Protista because they do not fit into any of the other three eukaryotic kingdoms; however, we can attempt to generally group them based on similarities to animals, plants and fungus. Thus, we will study the kingdom Protista in three sections: Animal-like protists, Plant-like protists, and Fungus-like protists. You will find that even some of the sample species we will investigate do not fit perfectly into any one of these categories, and you may find the same species discussed in a different section in the next text you encounter! When God designed the earth and all its inhabitants, he created an amazing diversity of species, each with its own purpose. While scientists may not agree about how to group all creatures, these microorganisms have continued to reproduce after their own kind since their creation.

Section Objectives

Review these objectives. When you have completed this section, you should be able to:

6. Discuss what characteristics set organisms of a particular kingdom apart from members of other kingdoms.

8. Describe some common forms of reproduction and/or locomotion of the microorganisms studied.

9. Discuss the economic and environmental impact of the groups of microorganisms.

10. Use proper technique to culture, observe, and identify microorganisms using a light microscope.

11. List and describe six phyla of animal-like protists.

Vocabulary

Study these words to enhance your learning success in this section.

cilia	cyst	taxis	gullet
motile	pellicle	dopodia	cytoplasm
flagellum	protozoan	phototaxis	Ciliophora
anal pore	chemotaxis	conjugation	phagocytosis
radiolarian	oral groove	homeostasis	Actinopoda
Foraminifera	Apicomplexa	oral groove	binary fission
food vacuole	apical complex	Zoomastigophora	
contractile vacuole		amoeboid movement	
pseucytoplasmic bridge		longitudinal binary fission	

ANIMAL-LIKE PROTISTS

Animal-like protists are commonly referred to as a group as protozoans. At some point in these organisms' life cycle, most protozoans are motile. A motile organism is capable of movement. In the past, protozoans were classified into a phylum based primarily on their means of motility. While we can still do so to some extent today, the study of molecular biology continues to have a great impact on the science of taxonomy and has contributed to the ever-changing classification of protozoa.

In this text, we will take a look at three phyla which move by using pseudopodia; Rhizopoda, Actinopoda, and Foraminifera. We will then take a look at phylum Ciliophora which move using cilia, and phylum Zoomastigophora which move by using flagella. We will then take a look at a phylum of protozoans which are not motile in their adult stage; the phylum Apicomplexa. As stated above, these six phyla may not be used by all scientists and may change as research continues.

Before we begin our study of the individual differences between the groupings, let's take a look at some structures and behaviors that are common to most protozoans. Protozoans live in fresh water, salt water, or in very wet environments. These wet living environments are very important to these single-celled organisms.

| Phagocytosis

Homeostasis. Homeostasis is the self-regulating exchange of water, dissolved materials, and dissolved gases between an organism and its surroundings. Like animals, protozoans need oxygen for survival, and they produce carbon dioxide which must be removed from the organism. This exchange of vital elements and waste products partially takes place directly through the cell membrane. However, water intake and excretion is regulated through a structure called a contractile vacuole. The ability of a protozoan to continually regulate its own internal conditions as its external conditions change is a marvelous, complex process.

Phagocytosis. Like the fungi we studied in the previous section, protozoans must get their food from their surroundings. While some protozoans are able to absorb some food directly through their cell membrane, most obtain food by means of a process called phagocytosis. This process begins when either the cell moves toward a tiny piece of food or the cell moves a tiny piece of food to a particular location along the cell membrane. The cell membrane encloses the food particle completely and forms a food vacuole. The food vacuole moves inside the cell where enzymes are secreted into the vacuole and the process of digestion takes place until the food particles are small enough to be used within the cell. The waste product is excreted from the cell. Refer to the Phagocytosis diagram showing a tiny virus being consumed by a type of protozoa called an amoeba.

Taxis. So, how does a tiny single-celled organism find its food? Why would God create this tiny creature with the ability to move? Many experiments have demonstrated that protozoans are capable of responding to stimuli in their environment. Taxis is defined as an organism's response to stimuli. In the case of protozoans, this response is usually either a complete change in direction or a change in the speed of movement. Chemotaxis is a response to the presence of a chemical. This is how a protozoan is able to find its food. Later, you

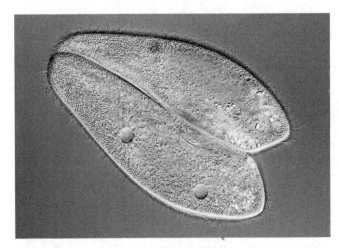

| Paramecium caudatum conjugation

will be introduced to a protist that will move in response to a change in light. This response is called phototaxis.

Reproduction: All protozoans are capable of asexual reproduction. Remember that this means only one parent is necessary for reproduction. Most protozoans reproduce asexually by a process called binary fission. Binary fission is the dividing of a mature parent cell to form two daughter cells. Binary fission starts when the nuclear material duplicates to make identical nuclei. Then the rest of the cytoplasm is divided to form two identical daughter cells. Cytoplasm is the content of a cell other than the nucleus. Typically, binary fission takes place only in ideal living conditions. When a protozoan is in a stressed environment, its metabolism may slow down, and it may form a protective outer covering called a cyst that will protect it until conditions improve again. Some protozoans are also capable of sexual reproduction where genetic material is shared between two individuals. Sexual reproduction in protozoans usually takes place by conjugation. In this process, two individual protozoa attach to each other and share genetic material. After the protozoa separate, each individual divides by fission creating four new individuals, each with a mixture of genetic material from two parent protozoa.

Complete these activities.

3.1 _____ is the general name for all animal-like protists.

3.2 Describe homeostasis and how contractile vacuoles are involved in the process.

_____

_____

_____

_____

3.3 Describe phagocytosis and how food vacuoles are involved in the process.

_____

_____

_____

3.4 List the six phyla of animal-like protists that you will be studying and their mode of motility.

a. _____

b. _____

c. _____

d. _____

e. _____

f. _____

3.5 In a eukaryotic cell, the nucleus and the _____ are the contents of

every cell. During binary fission, this material is divided between the two daughter cells.

3.6 Describe the process of conjugation. _____

_____

_____

_____

_____

_____

3.7 What is a cyst and why is it important to the survival of a particular species?

_____

_____

_____

LEARNING APPLICATION Part 1: Protozoan culture.

In the following activity, you will grow and observe a number of different protozoans taken from a "dirty" water source. You will need to start this activity today, then come back to complete it after 2 or 3 days have passed. If there is no open water source available when it is time to complete this project (such as winter months when everything may be frozen), you may want to consider purchasing a Protozoa Hatchery Kit from an education resource. (www.homesciencetools.com offers one at a reasonable price.)

For the opportunity to practice some field biology techniques, we strongly recommend you consider the collection of water samples an important part of this experience. Suggested "dirty" water sources include but are not limited to: a fresh-water pond or lake, a slow-moving stream or stagnant backwaters of a river, a rain puddle that has stood for a few days, or a bird bath. Be sure to choose a source that you can reach safely. You may need to get creative on how you obtain your samples!

These supplies are needed:

- 1 water collection container (quart jar)
- 4 small glass jars (baby food jars)
- "dirty" water source
- handful of hay or grass clippings

- 6 grains of rice
- pinch of hard-boiled egg yolk
- 1 tsp rich black soil (NOT potting soil)

Follow these directions. Put a check mark in the box when each step is completed.

Sample preparation:

☐ 1. Collect a large jar of "dirty" water.

☐ 2. Add one type of protozoa nutrient to each small jar and label each culture appropriately.
   a. Hay or grass clippings
   b. Rice
   c. Egg yolk
   d. Soil

☐ 3. Fill each jar about ¾ full of "dirty" water.

☐ 4. Set your cultures aside while you continue your LIFEPAC. After 3-5 days, check your cultures for any signs of change such as color change or cloudy looking water. When you observe these changes, you are ready to continue Part II of this activity.

TEACHER CHECK _____ _____
                                          initials   date

PHLA OF ANIMAL-LIKE PROTISTS

PHYLA RHIZOPODA, ACTINOPODA, AND FORAMINIFERA (AMOEBOID)

These first three groups of protozoa are very unique in their mode of movement. These organisms have an extremely flexible cell membrane that really does nothing to give them a definite shape. Instead, this flexible outer covering lends itself exceptionally well to amoeboid movement. Amoeboid movement is the capability of the cell to move simply by altering the consistency of its cytoplasm and allowing it to flow into structures called pseudopodia. Pseudopodia reach out and basically pull the rest of the cell after them. These "false feet" are not only used for movement; they also reach around a bacterium which has been located for food to form a food vacuole.

All species within these three phyla reproduce by means of binary fission. Sexual reproduction is not known to occur within these groups. Cyst formation is quite common by amoeboid organisms when living conditions are no longer optimal.

Amoeba proteus is a member of the phylum Rhizopoda that is typically found in abundance in fresh-water ponds. The previous diagram showing the process of phagocytosis is of an amoeba proteus. In a following activity, you will have the opportunity to study this species closer. Another species of the phylum Rhizopoda called *Entamoeba histolytica* is the cause of an intestinal infection in humans called amoebic dysentery.

Cysts formed by *E. histolytica* can live outside the human body and are easily transferred to other humans by houseflies and contaminated water sources. Symptoms of this infection include severe diarrhea that may lead to death if it is not treated. Amoebic dysentery is a serious concern for missionaries who are led to serve in developing countries where proper sanitation is lacking.

Organisms classified within the phyla Rhizopoda, Actinopoda, and Foraminifera are all capable of amoeboid movement. Members of the phyla Actinopoda and Foraminifera differ from members of the phylum Rhizopoda because they form a tiny shell outside their cell membrane. Actinopods form shells of mostly calcium carbonate (limestone). Foraminifers form shells of mostly silicon. These shells are as beautiful and as diverse as snowflakes. Each one has its own distinguishing pattern that includes tiny holes for the cytoplasm and cell membrane of the organism to reach through to form pseudopodia.

Foraminifers commonly called radiolarians are responsible for the make-up of much of the world's ocean floors. The glass-like silicon skeletons of radiolarians cover approximately one third of the ocean floor. In some places, these skeletal deposits are several hundred meters thick!

| Amoeba

| Foraminifers

Complete these activities.

3.8 Describe pseudopodia and their significance to an amoeboid protist. _____

_____

3.9 Discuss Entamoeba histolytica. _____

_____

_____

3.10 What is the main component of the tiny shells of the members of the phylum Actinopoda?

_____ Phylum Foraminifera? _____

3.11 _____ is the common name for foraminifers.

PHYLUM CILIOPHORA (CILIATES)

Members of the phylum Ciliophora move by using multiple tiny hair-like structures called cilia. Depending on the species, cilia may cover the entire surface of the single-celled organism, or they may be concentrated in certain areas on the cell surface. A ciliate moves its cilia in a constant beating action to control the direction and speed the organism is moving. This same beating action is also used to move food along the surface of the ciliate to the oral groove. The Oral groove of a ciliate is similar to the mouth of an animal.

We will take a look at a common inhabitant of fresh-water ponds called Paramecium caudatum as a representative of this phylum. Unlike the ever-changing shape of an amoeba, the paramecium has a distinctive shape. This shape is maintained by a firm yet elastic covering outside the cell membrane called a pellicle. Part of the shape maintained by the pellicle is an oval indentation called the oral groove. After a bacterium, a smaller protist, or a bit of organic material, has been moved by the cilia through the oral groove, it continues to the end of the gullet. At the end of the gullet, the food particle is surrounded by the cell membrane which then pinches off to form a food vacuole.

The food vacuole will move throughout the paramecium's cytoplasm as the food is digested. Waste product is released from the cell through the anal pore.

One feature of paramecium which makes it exceptional among eukaryotic cells is that it has two distinct nuclei. The larger, called the macronucleus, maintains the day-to-day activity of the cell. The macronucleus appears to be made up of multiple copies of the genetic material. The smaller nucleus, called the micronucleus, is important for sharing genetic data during sexual reproduction.

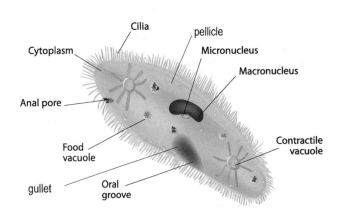

| Paramecium

Like the amoeba, paramecium can reproduce fairly quickly by binary fission. However, paramecia are also known to reproduce sexually by conjugation. In this process, two paramecia attach to each other at their oral surface where a cytoplasmic bridge connects them. Inside each cell, changes are made to the nuclear material in both the macronucleus and the micronucleus. At one point, genetic material crosses the cytoplasmic bridge between the micronuclei of each paramecium. Conjugation allows paramecium to create new combinations of genetic characteristics that may make the daughter cells more capable of survival in changing environments.

Complete these activities.

3.12 Describe cilia and their significance to a ciliate. _____

_____

_____

3.13 What structure is responsible for maintaining the consistent shape of a paramecium?

_____

3.14 Discuss the travels of a bacterium that has just been located as food by a paramecium. Be sure to include the names of the structures it will pass through.

_____

_____

_____

_____

_____

_____

3.15 What characteristic makes the cell of a paramecium exceptional compared to other eukaryotic cells? _____

_____

3.16 Describe conjugation between two paramecium. _____

_____

_____

_____

_____

_____

_____

PHYLUM ZOOMASTIGOPHORA (FLAGELLATES)

All members of the phylum Zoomastigophora travel by moving one or more long whip-like structures called flagellum. Members of this phylum are commonly referred to as zooflagellates. All zooflagellates are unicellular and most live in fresh-water ponds and lakes; however, quite a number also live inside other organisms, including humans. In fact, many human and animal diseases are attributed to zooflagellates.

The life cycles of zooflagellates vary quite a bit from one species to another. However, all undergo asexual reproduction at some point in their life cycle via binary fission. In contrast to the amoeba and paramecium, most zooflagellates undergo longitudinal binary fission to produce two daughter cells that are mirror images of each other. Many of the parasitic species also include cyst formation in their life cycle. Often, these cysts are the only way that the zooflagellate can exist outside of a host;

thus the cyst is the means that an infection can be passed from person to person. In many human diseases, it is the cyst that is ingested from contaminated sources, such as drinking water, food, swimming pools, or even dirty hands.

Interestingly, many species which cause human diseases include a life cycle with an insect vector. An insect vector is an insect that is responsible for passing a disease from one human to another. Sometimes the species which the insect vector transmits actually completes a portion of its life cycle inside the insect; and sometimes the insect simply acts as the carrier when cysts stick to the feet or mouthparts of the insect. For example, the tsetse fly found only in Africa is the insect vector for Trypanosoma, the zooflagellate which causes African sleeping sickness. See the following diagram for the life cycle of the Trypanosoma.

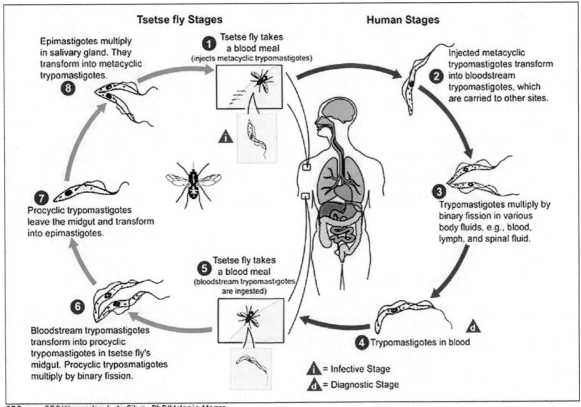

CDC.gov: CDC/Alexander J. da Silva, PhD/Melanie Moser

| Trypanosoma life cycle

The following table lists a few other human diseases attributed to zooflagellates.

SPECIES (OR GENUS)	DISEASE	DESCRIPTION	COMMON LOCATION	VECTOR
Trypanosoma brucei	African sleeping sickness	Affects the central nervous system. Causes sleepiness, weakness, and possible coma.	Africa	tsetse fly (only lives in Africa)
Giardia lamblia	Giardiasis or "Hiker's disease"	Intestinal disease which causes diarrhea, flatulence, stomach cramping, and sometimes nausea.	Common to hiker's who drink contaminated water. Spreads easily in child daycare settings.	often water - water borne cysts
Leishmania donovani	Leishmaniasis	Large open sores on the skin or similar sores on internal organs such as the liver, spleen, or bone marrow.	Mostly tropical and subtropical settings.	phlebotomine sand fly
Trypanosoma cruzi	Chagas' disease	Initial symptoms are often mild such as fever, fatigue, loss of appetite, and diarrhea. Longterm damage can include cardiac and/or chronic intestinal problems.	Mexico, Central and South America. Common where poorly–built houses exist.	triatomine bug or 'kissing bug'

Another group of zooflagellates which has an enormous economic significance all over the world is of the genus *Trichonympha*. Members of this phylum live in a symbiotic relationship with termites. As you know, termites are destructive little insects that cause damage to houses and many other structures built from wood. Although the termite's main food source is wood, the termite is not able to digest the wood! The *Trichonympha* must live in the termites gut and digest the wood for the termite. In this way, both the termite and the *Trichonympha* are fed by the termite's meal.

Complete these activities.

3.17 Zooflagellates move by means of a whip-like structure called a _____ .

3.18 What two locations does this text suggest you might find zooflagellates living in?

a. _____   b. _____

3.19 How does longitudinal binary fission differ from other forms of binary fission?

_____

3.20 Discuss the two ways in which insect vectors carry a disease from one human to another.

_____

_____

3.21 Name the human disease and the vector of each zooflagellate.

Giardia lamblia _____ _____

Leishmania donovani _____ _____

Trypanosoma cruzi _____ _____

Trypanosoma brucei _____ _____

3.22 Describe the relationship between a termite and Trichonympha. _____

_____

_____

_____

PHYLUM APICOMPLEXA (SPORE FORMING)

Unlike the other groups of protozoans we have studied so far, members of the phylum Apicomplexa do not have a specific apparatus for locomotion or movement. Species within this phylum are unique because, at some point in their life cycle, they form spores. At another place in their life cycle, a structure called an **apical complex** exists. The apical complex is a key structure for these parasites to be able to enter and interact with their host cells. All species in this phylum are parasitic. The complicated life cycles of many species involve a vector and an animal or human host.

As an example from this phylum, we will study one of the most heavily researched organisms in the world, the organism that causes malaria. According to a World Health Organization Report in 2015, an estimated 214 million cases of malaria occur every year. It's no wonder that this disease has the interest of thousands of scientists! Most of these cases occur in tropical and subtropical regions of the world, often in developing countries.

Malaria is a devastating disease caused by four known species in humans: _Plasmodium falciparum, Plasmodium vivax, Plasmodium ovale, and_

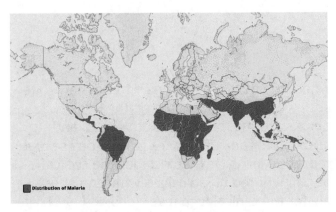

| Worldwide distribution of malaria

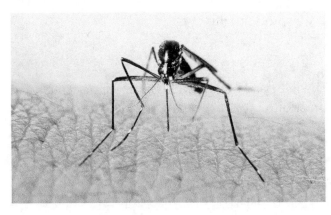

Plasmodium malariae. The most common symptom of malaria is a cycle of very severe fever alternating with chills. The *Plasmodium* life cycle includes an insect vector and a human host. While there are treatments, the best way of limiting the affects of malaria is to effectively control its insect vector, the *Anopheles* mosquito.

You can see in the following diagram that the Plasmodium life cycle includes three stages, the exo-erythrocytic cycle, the erythrocytic cycle, and the sporogonic cycle.

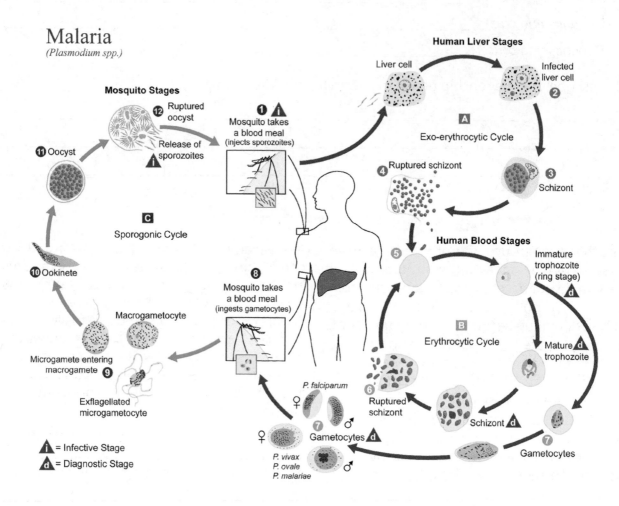

| Plasmodium life cycle

The life cycle begins when a female *Anopheles* mosquito bites a human and the *Plasmodium* sporozoite enters the human in the mosquito's saliva. The sporozoite makes its way through the human host's bloodstream to the liver where the exo-erythrocytic cycle begins inside the liver cells. The products of this cycle, the merozoites are released back into the blood

where the next cycle begins. After a merozoite enters a red blood cell, the erythrocytic cycle begins. During this stage, both sexual and asexual reproduction takes place. The asexual reproduction cycle that includes the cyclical bursting of red blood cells is what is responsible for the clinical high fever followed by chills of the human patient. The sexual reproduction cycle is what releases spores called microgametocytes and macrogametocytes into the bloodstream. When a mosquito bites and takes a blood meal from an infected human, these spores enter the mosquito, where they begin the next stage, the sporogonic cycle. The end product of the sporogonic cycle is the sporozoites in the mosquito's saliva. When the next human host is bitten by the vector mosquito, the cycle begins again.

There are numerous other diseases caused by members of the phylum Apicomplexa. Many of them are intestinal diseases that cause diarrhea and other unsettling intestinal symptoms in humans as well as many domestic animals such as cats, dogs, chickens, sheep, and cattle. Farmers are often faced with large expenses associated with treating and controlling these infections in livestock.

Another serious disease from this group of microorganisms is known as toxoplasmosis. Toxoplasmosis is caused by the protozoan parasite *Toxoplasma gondii*. This parasite can live in birds, mice, domestic cats, and humans. Many doctors caution pregnant mothers to avoid their cat's litter box as a precautionary measure to avoid exposure to spores that may be in the cat's feces. While an infection of healthy adults rarely causes any serious complications, babies who are exposed to the parasite while they are still in their mother's womb are much more susceptible to serious consequences. Babies born after infection may have severe brain damage at birth or, in 50-75% of the cases, the child may develop mental handicaps later in life as a result of infection while in the womb.

Complete these activities.

3.23 All species of the phylum Apicomplexa are _____ .

3.24 What is one known function of the apical complex? _____

_____

3.25 What is the importance of the sexual and asexual portions of the erythrocytic cycle of the

Plasmodium life cycle? _____

_____

_____

_____

_____

_____

_____

3.26 The _____ mosquito is the insect vector for malaria.

3.27 Which group of humans is likely to experience the most devastating symptoms of

toxoplasmosis? _____

View These 1003 Clips: Microscope: Amoeba, Microscope: Paramecium, Microscope: Euglena, Microscope: Nostoc, and Microscope: Spirogyra, from the 10th Grade SCIENCE EXPERIMENTS Video

LEARNING APPLICATION Part 2: Protozoan culture.

When your four cultures show some indication of change such as color change or cloudiness, you may continue with Part II of this activity. If you are unable to locate any protozoans when you first continue this activity, it may need to wait a few additional days and try again. You should plan on completing this activity within 2 weeks from initially creating the cultures, as they may not grow indefinitely.

These supplies are needed:

- cotton ball
- microscope
- medicine dropper
- depression slide
- cover slips
- protozoan cultures

Follow these directions. Put a check mark in the box when each step is completed.

Sample preparation:

☐ 1. Prepare a slide by adding a drop of water from your first culture solution to a depression slide. If necessary, add a tiny amount of cotton strands to your slide to create barriers which may slow down some organisms. Place a cover slip over your sample.

☐ 2. Scan your sample using low power. You may be able to view some slow-moving organisms using high power.

☐ 3. In the space provided, sketch all the different kinds of organisms you are able to find in each culture. Describe in detail what you observe with each culture. Be sure to sketch and document ALL organisms you see. They may not all be protozoans.

a. Hay or grass clippings culture:

_____

_____

_____

_____

_____

_____

_____

_____

SCIENCE 1003

LIFEPAC TEST

NAME _____

DATE _____

SCORE _____

SCIENCE 1003: LIFEPAC TEST

Match these items (each answer, 3 points).

1. _____ binary fission
2. _____ virulence
3. _____ pathogen
4. _____ conjugation
5. _____ fermentation
6. _____ symbiosis
7. _____ motile
8. _____ host
9. _____ ocular lens
10. _____ budding
11. _____ homeostasis
12. _____ lysis

a. plant or animal which supports a parasite
b. magnifying structure found in the eyepiece
c. able to move independently
d. asexual reproduction of yeast by pinching-off
e. rupturing of a cell
f. self-regulating process to maintain water level
g. mutually positive arrangement between species
h. ability of a virus to cause disease
i. organism or substance which causes disease
j. asexual reproduction in which parent cell divides in two
k. sexual reproduction in some protozoans
l. breakdown of complex molecules into simpler ones

Answer true or false (each answer, 3 points).

13. _____ Members of kingdom Eubacteria are eukaryotes.

14. _____ One reason fungi are no longer classified as plants is the presence of chitin in their cell walls.

15. _____ A virus is a prokaryote.

16. _____ A halophile is responsible for spoiling juices.

17. _____ Viruses are capable of replication outside the host cell.

18. _____ Algin is a useful substance derived from brown algae

Match the scientific name with the description (each answer, 3 points).

19. _____ Karenia brevis

20. _____ Penicillium chrysogenum

21. _____ Plasmodium vivax

22. _____ Phytophthora infestans

23. _____ Borrelia burgdorferi

24. _____ Agaricus bisporis

a. fungi known for the production of an antibiotic

b. water mold which causes late blight in potatoes

c. dinoflagellate responsible for red tide by Florida

d. common mushrooms found in grocery stores

e. bacteria responsible for Lyme disease

f. protozoan known to cause malaria

Write the letter for the correct answer (each answer, 2 points).

25. The Englishman, _____ , first used the term "cells" to describe tiny compartments which made up cork.
    a. Galileo
    c. Robert Hooke
    b. Anton van Leeuwenhoek
    d. Edward Jenner

26. The microorganisms commonly found living on the human skin are known as _____ .
    a. latent infection   b. pathogens   c. normal flora   d. thallus

27. The tiny exoskeleton of a diatom is mostly composed of _____ .
    a. calcium carbonate   b. silicon   c. nucleic acid   d. starch

28. Methanogens are able to live in an _____ environment.
    a. extremely salty   b. extremely acidic   c. extremely hot   d. anaerobic

29. The members of kingdom Archaea which live in the Dead Sea are known as _____ .
    a. spirochetes   b. thermoacidophiles   c. halophiles   d. attenuated

30. Multicellular fungi are composed of thread-like structures called _____ which group together to form mycelia to perform specific functions.
    a. hyphae   b. cilia   c. sporangium   d. rhizoids

31. A pathogenic RNA molecule is called a _____ .
    a. prion   b. capsid   c. virion   d. viroid

32. A bacteria culture that has a high concentration of _____ in the cell wall will stain Gram-positive.
    a. peptidoglycan   b. nucleic acid   c. spores   d. protein

Complete these activities.

33. List the five steps of a lytic viral replication cycle in order. (5 points)

    a. _____

    b. _____

    c. _____

    d. _____

    e. _____

34. Discuss malaria, one of the most heavily researched organisms in the world.
    Include: the scientific genus of the microorganism; the insect vector; and at least three other
    details about malaria. (4 points)

    _____

    _____

    _____

    _____

    _____

    _____

35. Name three limitations to using an electron microscope to view an organism? (3 points)

    a. _____

    b. _____

    c. _____

b. Rice:

_____

_____

_____

_____

_____

_____

_____

c. Egg yolk:

_____

_____

_____

_____

_____

_____

_____

d. Soil:

_____

_____

_____

_____

_____

_____

_____

(Continued on next page)

4. **Write your answers on the blank lines.** Compare and explain why there may have been a different population of organisms in each culture.

If you were to repeat this activity, what would you do differently to improve your results?

_____   _____

_____   _____

_____   _____

_____   _____

_____   _____

_____   _____

_____   _____

_____   _____

_____   _____

_____   _____

_____   _____

_____   _____

TEACHER CHECK _____ _____

initials   date

Review the material in this section in preparation for the Self Test. This Self Test will check your mastery of this particular section as well as your knowledge of all previous sections.

SELF TEST 3

Match these definitions (each answer, 3 points).

3.01	_____ eukaryote	a. obtain food from non-living organic material
3.02	_____ taxis	b. mutually positive arrangement between species
3.03	_____ radiolarian	c. response to a chemical
3.04	_____ host	d. response to light
3.05	_____ resolving power	e. member of phylum Foraminifera
3.06	_____ chemotaxis	f. organism's response to a stimulus
3.07	_____ conjugation	g. cell with membrane-bound structures
3.08	_____ symbiosis	h. ability to tell two points apart
3.09	_____ saprophyte	i. organism in which a parasite is growing
3.010	_____ phototaxis	j. sexual reproduction in some protozoans

Fill in the blanks (each answer, 3 points).

What structure does each organism utilize for mobility (_flagellum, cilia, pseudopodia_)?

3.011 Ciliophora _____

3.012 _Giardia lamblia_ _____

3.013 Rhizopoda _____

3.014 _Entamoeba histolytica_ _____

3.015 _Paramecium caudatum_ _____

3.016 Zoomastigophora _____

3.017 Actinopoda _____

3.018 _Trichonympha_ _____

Write the letter for the correct answer on each blank (each answer, 3 points).

3.019 Which structure is not part of the process of phagocytosis in a ciliate? _____
a. oral groove   b. cytoplasmic bridge c. gullet   d. food vacuole

3.020 The members of the phylum _____ are all parasitic.
a. Chytridiomycota   b. Zoomastigophora c. Actinopoda   d. Apicomplexa

3.021 The insect vector for Plasmodium vivax is the _____ .
a. Anopheles mosquito
b. phlebotomine sand fly
c. kissing bug
d. tsetse fly

3.022 _____ is the structure within a protozoan where enzymes are secreted to digest food.
a. Contractile vacuole
b. Gullet
c. Food vacuole
d. Oral groove

3.023 The total magnification of a microscope with a 15x ocular lens and a 20x objective lens is _____ .
a. 35x
b. 600x
c. 350x
d. 300x

3.024 In common mold, the _____ is the tiny stalk-like structure that support the fruiting bodies where spores are produced and released.
a. stolon
b. stem
c. sporangium
d. sporangiophore

3.025 The _____ of a microscope can be rotated to change the amount of light that is allowed to enter the microscope.
a. diaphragm
b. eyepiece
c. fine adjustment knob
d. revolving nosepiece

3.026 Who is credited with inventing the electron microscope? _____
a. Anton van Leeuwenhoek
b. Charles A. Spencer
c. Max Knott and Ernst Ruska
d. Sir Alexander Fleming

3.027 The break-down of complex molecules into simpler ones is called _____ .
a. binary fission
b. symbiosis
c. phagocytosis
d. fermentation

3.028 The kingdom _____ contains prokaryotic organisms.
a. Plantae
b. Eubacteria
c. Fungi
d. Protista

Complete these items (each numbered item, 8 points).

3.029 Briefly describe how the two parts of the Plasmodium erythrocytic cycle affect the human

host. _____

_____

3.030 Choose one microscopic species that causes a human illness. Give the scientific name of the species, the disease it causes, the vector, and briefly describe the symptoms.

_____

_____

80
/ 100   SCORE _____   TEACHER _____ _____
                                                        initials   date

4. PLANT-LIKE PROTISTS

Plant-like protists are commonly known as algae. Like plants, algae are capable of producing their own food source through photosynthesis. In the past, algae were commonly classified in the kingdom Plantae. This is no longer the case because of significant differences in reproductive features between plant species and algae species. Also, unlike most plants, algae do not have true vascular parts such as roots, stems, and leaves.

Section Objectives

Review these objectives. When you have completed this section, you should be able to:

8. Describe some common forms of reproduction and/or locomotion of the microorganisms studied.

9. Discuss the economic and environmental impact of the groups of microorganisms.

12. List and describe seven phyla of plant-like protists (algae).

Vocabulary

Study these words to enhance your learning success in this section.

phycology	brown algae	kelp	thallus
phycoerythrin	kelp forest	euglena	agar
green algae	fucoxanthin	algin	water mold
sulcus	carrageenan	red algae	diatoms
red eyespot	euglenoid movement	aethalium	slug phase
feeding phase	plasmodium	golden-brown algae	late blight
algal bloom	dinoflagellates	diatomaceous earth	red tide
daughter colonies	cellular slime mold	plasmodial slime mold	

PHYLA OF PLANT-LIKE PROTISTS (ALGAE)

Algae are a very diverse group of organisms ranging from single-celled organisms to complex multicellular organisms. They can be found in almost anywhere on earth, including on trees and in the soil; however, most live in either fresh water or salt water.

Species of algae are known for their diversity and their beauty. While there is no way we could study all 30,000 species of algae, in this LIFEPAC section, we will take a look at seven different phyla of algae and how members in each phylum are important to us as humans.

The study of algae is called phycology. You will soon see why this is a very important area of biological research.

Did you know that 70% to 90% of all oxygen produced in the earth's atmosphere is a result of the photosynthesis performed by algae? We know that plants and trees on land are also responsible for the production of oxygen, but to think that *most oxygen production on earth* comes from organisms too small to be seen without a microscope is amazing! Most of us are familiar with the annoying aspects of algae; maybe the green "goo" growing in your home aquarium, the green scum that grows over your favorite fishing hole, the constant battle to keep your swimming pool clear. Do you enjoy a snack of pudding or ice cream? A component of algae may be an ingredient in your favorite snack.

The following table lists the phylum of algae we will take a brief look at in this LIFEPAC section. You will notice that for the most part, the phyla are created based on the thallus, the cell wall structure, and the type of food storage. The body structure of an alga is called the thallus. The common thalli for algae are: unicellular, colonial, filamentous, and multicellular.

PHYLUM	COMMON NAME	THALLUS	COMMON ENVIRONMENT	APPROX. SPECIES	CELL WALL	FOOD STORAGE
Chlorophyta	Green Algae	Most Unicellular (some simple colonies and a few multicellular)	Fresh water, terrestrial	7,000	Cellulose	Starch
Rhodophyta	Red Algae	Multicellular	Marine - most in warm shallow waters, some in deep waters	4,000	Calcium carbonate, cellulose, pectin	Starch
Phaeophyta	Brown Algae	Multicellular	Marine - cold waters	1,500	Cellulose, algin	Complex carbohydrate
Euglenophyta	Euglena	Unicellular	Fresh water	1,000	None - Pellicle	Carbohydrate
Chrysophyta	Golden-Brown Algae	Most Unicellular, some colonies	Fresh water, some marine	1,000	Cellulose	Oil
Bacillariophyta	Diatoms	Most Unicellular	Any moist environment	12,500	Silicon	Oil
Pyrrophyta	Fire Algae / Dinoflagellates	Unicellular (some form simple colonies)	Marine, some fresh water	1,100	Cellulose	Starch

| Phyla of plant-like protists

PHYLUM CHLOROPHYTA (GREEN ALGAE)

Members of the phylum Chlorophyta include the species that we most commonly refer to as green algae. However, don't let the single name deceive you. Green algae are so diverse that one might wonder how they could all be classified in the same phylum. This phylum contains members with all types of thalli, although most species are unicellular. Like most species in the kingdom Plantae, green algae have cell walls made of cellulose and store food in the form of starch. Green algae are typically found in fresh water such as lakes, ponds, and the backwaters of rivers; however, there are also a number of terrestrial species that live on rocks, on tree bark, and even in snow. A few green algae are marine (salt water) species.

Cladophora vagabunda is multicellular green alga that is a nuisance to individuals who enjoy aquarium fish tanks in their homes. Regular cleaning and maintenance is necessary to keep this and many other green algae species in check in a home aquarium.

Look at the image of a *Spirogyra*, which is a green alga species. On the surface of stagnant water, the colonies of these filamentous algae can look like a green carpet. Under a microscope, you can see where this alga gets its name. The chloroplasts in each cell are spiral shaped.

These next photos are of *Volvox* colonies. The image shows numerous daughter colonies inside. At some point in the replication process, this parent colony will break open and release each of the daughter colonies to exist on its own. These beautiful, complicated spherical colonies are made up of thousands of individual flagellated alga. Each individual Volvox cell has a red eyespot present which is capable of detecting light. Amazingly, the entire colony is

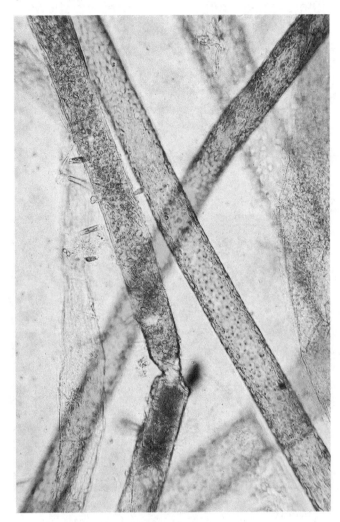

| Cladophora vagabunda

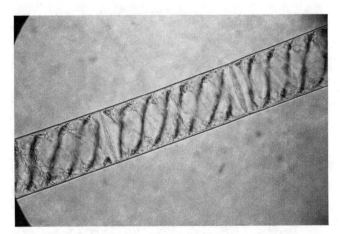

| Spirogyra under 40x magnification

capable of phototaxis as one unit. The second photo is taken much, much closer and shows the tiny individual strands of cytoplasm which hold the individual cells in place in the colony.

Chlamydomonas nivalis or "Watermelon snow" is unicellular green algae which thrive in snow. Do you see anything strange about these green algae? They're not green at all! Chlamydomonas is often found during summer months at higher elevations where the snow cover remains, such as the highest elevations in Yosemite National Park in California. Besides the green chlorophyll in these algae, they also contained carotenoids, the same type of pigment that gives color to tomatoes and carrots. Believe it or not, watermelon snow actually smells like watermelon, too!

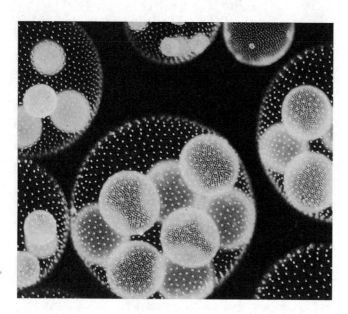

| Volvox

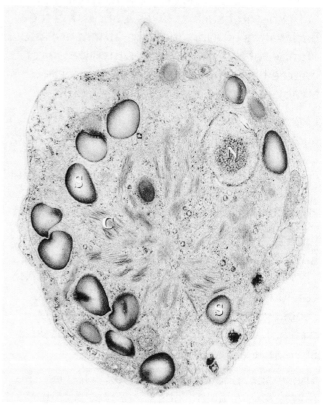

| Chlamydomonas nivalis

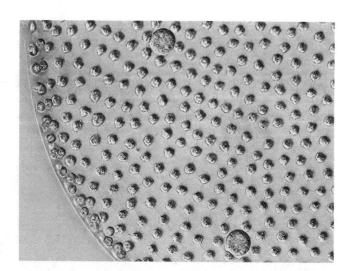

| Close-up of Volvox

Complete these activities.

4.1 What characteristic makes algae plant-like? Why are they not part of the kingdom Plantae?

_____

_____

4.2 List four common thallus of algae.

a. _____ b. _____

c. _____ d. _____

4.3 The study of algae is called _____ .

4.4 Which two characteristics of green algae are also common in plants? _____

_____

4.5 What is the thallus type of Cladophora vagabunda? _____

4.6 What is the thallus type of Volvox? _____

4.7 What pigment is responsible for the color of watermelon snow? _____

PHYLUM RHODOPHYTA (RED ALGAE)

Species in the phylum Rhodophyta are commonly known as **red algae**. Red algae are almost all multicellular and marine. Because of the presence of a pigment called **phycoerythrin**, most rhodophytes (red algae) show various shades of red. Phycoerythrin is able to absorb blue light that can penetrate deeper into water than most of the light spectrum; thus, red algae grows at greater depths than most green algae. Certain species of red algae are important for the materials they produce. For example, some red algae species are able to remove calcium from the sea water. The calcium deposited by these living organisms is very important in the process of building coral reefs. Two other substances derived from red algae are **carrageenan** and **agar**. Carrageenan is commonly used in the food-processing industry as an ingredient in many foods, such as ice cream and marshmallows. Agar is used by scientists and medical professionals as a food source for growing bacteria in the laboratory.

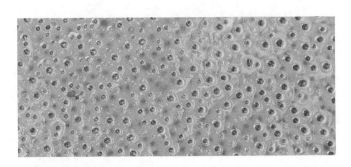

| Red algae

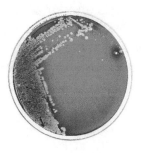

| Bacteria colonies on blood agar

PHYLUM PHAEOPHYTA (BROWN ALGAE)

Species in the phylum Phaeophyta are generally known as brown algae. Like red algae, brown algae species are almost all multicellular and marine. Phaeophytes (brown algae) contain a pigment called fucoxanthin which gives them their brown color. Some giant species of brown algae live in deeper colder water, while some smaller species live right along the shore and may be completely exposed during low tides.

Algin is a gelatin-like substance used in the food-processing industry that is derived from brown algae. While algin is not chemically the same as carrageenan, it is used for some of the same purposes.

A couple other brown algae groups we will mention are; *Laminaria*, commonly known as kelp, and Sargassum. Kelp acts somewhat like trees in the giant kelp forests of the ocean. These kelp forests are very important ecosystems just like the terrestrial forests we are more familiar with on land because many plants and animals thrive in these kelp forests. Several well-known kelp forests exist just off the coast of California from San Diego to Santa Cruz.

On the other side of the Americas, you will find another area well-known for brown algae, the Sargasso Sea. This area east of Florida is very salty and has comparatively calm winds and currents. *Sargassum* is floating kelp that thrives in these conditions. Christopher Columbus documented the large amounts of seaweed when he navigated this portion of the Atlantic Ocean. Even today, the Sargasso Sea is often avoided by sailors because of the possibility of getting the ship tangled and stranded in the brown seaweed.

| Underwater kelp forest at Catalina Island, California

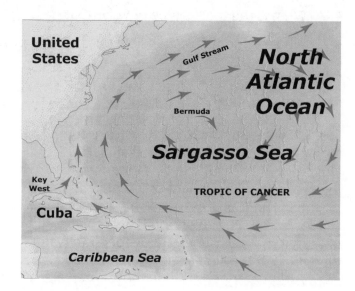

Write the answers on the blanks.

4.8 _____ is the pigment that gives red algae its color and

_____ is the pigment that gives brown algae its color.

4.9 Name two substances derived from algae that are commonly used as thickeners in the food

processing industry. a. _____ b. _____

4.10 Briefly describe the following locations.

kelp forest _____

Sargasso Sea _____

4.11 Give the scientific name of these algae.

kelp _____

algae Columbus encountered in the Sargasso Sea _____

PHYLUM EUGLENOPHYTA (EUGLENA)

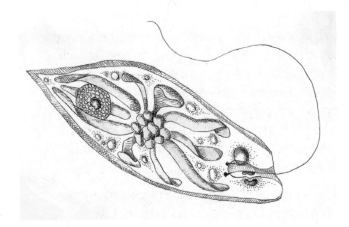

| Euglena

This group of unicellular organisms has probably given scientists more trouble than any other group in trying to figure out where they fit taxonomically. Euglenophytes, commonly known as euglena, have in the past been classified with the protozoans, the animal-like protists. One reason for this previous classification was that euglenas are motile, usually with two flagella.

The second reason for being classified with the protozoans is: like the protozoan Paramecium, euglenas do not have a cell wall; instead, they have a flexible outer covering called a pellicle. Also, like other protozoans, euglenas are able to regulate their internal water level because of the presence of contractile vacuoles. Today, most taxonomic systems include euglena with the plant-like protists in a phylum all their own. Like other algae, euglenas produce their own food using photosynthesis; however, euglenas

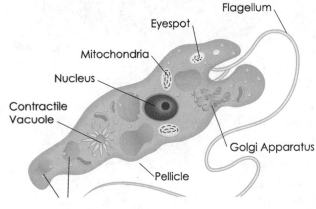

| Diagram of an euglena

have the unique capability of surviving in low light because they can also take in nutrients from their environments. Euglenas have a red eyespot which allows each organism to move toward a light source.

Interestingly, the flagella on a euglena are on the anterior end of the cell. This means that rather than having the movement push from the rear of the organism, the flagella act to pull the euglena through the water from the front. Euglenas are also capable of moving along a solid surface in a way very similar to a worm that inches its way along. A euglena accomplishes this movement basically by scrunching itself up, then stretching itself out. This unique movement is called **euglenoid movement**.

Write the answers on the blanks.

4.12 List three reasons that euglena have been classified as a protozoan in the past.

a. _____

b. _____

c. _____

4.13 Describe euglenoid movement. _____

_____

PHYLUM CHRYSOPHYTA (GOLDEN-BROWN ALGAE)

| Golden-brown algae

Many species of the phylum Chrysophyta are similar in many ways to the unicellular and colonial green algae. This group is commonly known as **golden-brown algae**. This distinct color is the result of green chlorophyll along with varying levels of carotenoids as we saw in the watermelon snow. Unlike green algae which store their food in the form of starches, golden-brown algae store food as oil droplets throughout the cytoplasm. Though golden-brown algae produce most of their food via photosynthesis, they are also capable of obtaining nutrients directly from their surroundings like the euglena.

This image is of a colonial species of golden-brown algae known as *Synura*. Like most golden-brown algae, each *Synura* cell in the colony is flagellated. The flagella surround the colony, and the entire colony is able to move in a smooth rolling or tumbling action through the water. This species is found in fresh-water ponds, lakes, and slow-moving streams.

Another unicellular golden-brown algae is *Ochromonas*. Each cell has two flagella, a red eyespot, and one or two plate-like golden-brown chloroplasts where the photosynthesis occurs. Many *Ochromonas* species thrive in lake water that has very low nutrient levels where many other algae species are not able to grow. In other words, these golden-brown algae are typically found in very clean lakes. A few common *Ochromonas* species are marine species.

PHYLUM BACILLARIOPHYTA (DIATOMS)

The phylum Bacillariophyta contains approximately one third of all algae species, more than any other phylum of algae. It's no wonder that members of this phylum, commonly known as diatoms, are found just about anywhere on earth where there is moisture. However, you will not see an individual diatom without the help of a microscope. Four individual diatoms laid side by side are approximately the width of a piece of human hair, but the intricate design of each individual is completely amazing and worth looking for with a microscope! Each diatom is encased in an intricate three-dimensional glass-like structure made mostly of silicon. These "glass houses" of geometric patterns are actually made up of two halves that fit perfectly together around the living organism like a tiny gift box. While studying the perfectly symmetrical design of more than 10,000 species of diatoms, a person gets a small sense of God's perfect creation.

Diatoms are some of the most important organisms in the entire world's ecosystem. They are abundant throughout the world's oceans, including areas of the ocean where the water is too cold for other algae to grow. These vast numbers of diatoms contribute to the earth's atmospheric oxygen supply and act as a primary food source in the aquatic food chain. In fact, it is estimated that 90% of all living organisms in the world's oceans are diatoms!

The silicon exoskeletons of deceased diatoms are also very important to us as humans today. Diatomaceous earth, terrestrial deposits made mostly of fossilized diatoms during the great flood, have many functions in society. Diatomaceous earth is commonly mined and processed for use as a mild abrasive, an insulator, and use in filtration systems. Even the stabilizing ingredient in dynamite comes from diatomaceous earth!

Diatoms commonly reproduce asexually through binary fission. When binary fission takes place, one half of the "gift box" structure goes with each daughter cell, and the other half then forms in perfect symmetry to the original, but slightly smaller. As binary fission continues over time, the daughter cells get smaller and smaller. At some point, various diatoms will shed their outer shell to grow, then will form a new larger silica encasement.

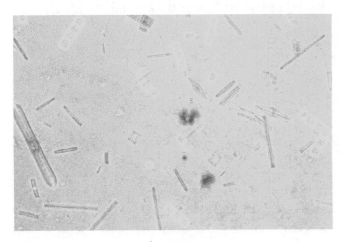

| Mixed diatoms magnified 100x

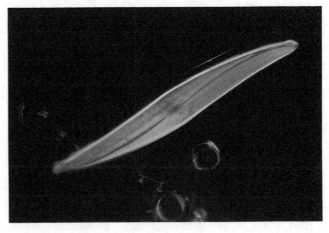

| Diatoms magnified 400x

Complete these activities.

4.14 What two pigments together create the color in golden-brown algae?_____

_____

4.15 Describe a Synura colony. _____

_____

4.16 What type of water is the presence of Ochromonas an indication of? Why? _____

_____

_____

4.17 Where are you likely to find diatoms? _____

4.18 In what form do golden-brown algae and diatoms store their food? _____

4.19 The three-dimensional glass-like structure encasing each diatom is composed mostly of

_____ .

4.20 List three uses for diatomaceous earth. _____

_____

PHYLUM PYRROPHYTA (DINOFLAGELLATES)

The final group of algae, phylum Pyrrophyta, is composed of unicellular algae that typically have two flagella, of two different lengths. The longer flagellum is used in a whirling action to produce movement. The shorter flagellum remains inside a groove called the sulcus. The shorter flagellum is thought to act more like a rudder to help direct which way the organism moves. Each individual also has two cell wall plates composed of cellulose which overlap and act like armor plates. Species within the phylum Pyrrophyta are commonly called dinoflagellates, which means "whirling flagella."

We will take a look at the species *Karenia brevis*, an algae common along the Gulf Coast of Florida as a representative dinoflagellate. This dinoflagellate is always present in the Gulf of Mexico; however, when an algal bloom or red tide occurs, the adverse effects are extensive. An algal bloom is a rapid extensive growth of algae as a result of nearly perfect growing conditions in a particular location. These Florida red tides (algal blooms of dinoflagellates) occur almost every season; however, the size, extent, and severity of the damage varies greatly from year to year.

The November 1978 red tide bloom off the coast of Florida created economic losses estimated between $15 and $25 million. Much of

| Algal bloom

this loss is as a result of a neurotoxin given off by the *Karenia brevis* algae. This neurotoxin is responsible for giant fish kills during and immediately after a red tide. Also, this same neurotoxin is known to cause a human condition called Neurotoxic Shellfish Poisoning (NSP) if shell fish are eaten from the area affected by the red tide. NSP symptoms include nausea, diarrhea, dizziness, and numbness of tongue, lips, and throat. Not only do the fishermen and harvesters of shellfish suffer as a result of a red tide, but the businesses that depend on the waters for tourism and recreational activities also suffer.

 Write the answers on the blanks.

4.21 Describe the two flagella of a dinoflagellate and their functions. _____

_____

_____

4.22 What is an algal bloom? _____

_____

4.23 List at least 4 businesses that are negatively affected by a severe red tide in the Gulf Coast of

Florida. _____

_____

_____

4.24 How would a tourist in Florida become sick with NSP? _____

_____

FUNGUS-LIKE PROTISTA

So far in your study of the kingdom Protista, you have been introduced to a group of animal-like protists known as protozoans and a group of plant-like protists known as algae. The final collection within the kingdom Protista is the group of fungus-like protists. We will take a brief look at three phyla of fungus-like protists: Myxomycota, Acrasiomycota, and Oomycota. The phyla Myxomycota and Acrasiomycota include organisms known as slime molds. The phylum Oomycota contains organisms commonly known as water molds and downy molds.

PHYLA OF FUNGUS-LIKE PROTISTS

Contrary to the common names used, these organisms are not classified in the kingdom Fungi, like true molds you studied earlier in this LIFEPAC. Two reasons that these organisms are not considered fungus are: first, their cell walls (when present) are composed of cellulose, while the cell walls of fungus are composed of chitin; second, at some point in their life cycle, these fungus-like protists are motile, making them more animal-like during that phase of their life cycle.

Similar to true fungi, fungus-like protists have a fairly complicated life cycle that usually includes sexual and asexual reproductive phases. Water molds and downy molds have a stage in their life cycle when they exist as individual flagellated cells. On the other hand, slime molds live part of their life cycle as amoeba-like cells.

PHYLUM ACRASIOMYCOTA (CELLULAR SLIME MOLDS)

Cellular slime mold is grouped in the phylum Acrasiomycota. These organisms are commonly found in cool moist environments where a large amount of decomposing organic matter exists. If you are interested in slime mold hunting, try looking on the cool floor of a forest, on the wood mulch around a landscaped home during cool, wet weather, or even simply in your amply-watered lawn.

During one phase of the cellular slime mold's life cycle, commonly called the feeding phase, the organism exists as individual amoeba-like cells that actively feed on organic material, bacteria, and fungus. When food becomes scarcer, or other growing conditions are no longer favorable, some individual cells emit a chemical that other slime mold cells react to (chemotaxis) by gathering into a larger, single slimy mass. This phase in the life cycle of cellular slime mold is sometimes called the slug phase because the single mass of individual cells looks and acts similar to a slug. It is from this slug-like structure that fruiting bodies

similar to those formed by fungus will evolve. Individual spores released from the fruiting bodies are capable of becoming new individual amoeba-like cells, and the cycle begins again.

PHYLUM MYXOMYCOTA (PLASMODIAL SLIME MOLDS)

Plasmodial slime molds belong to the phylum Myxomycota. Plasmodial slime molds can be found in the same types of environments as cellular slime molds; however, they are more common, with approximately 500 known species. There are less than 100 known cellular slime mold species.

Plasmodial slime mold differs from cellular slime mold in a few key ways in its life cycle. Plasmodial slime molds exist in their feeding phase as a multi-nucleated plasmodium. In this phase, each individual cell loses its cell membranes, forming a large mass of cytoplasm with up to millions of individual nuclei floating freely within. This mass is able to move along a surface in search of food in an amoeba-like fashion by extending pseudopodia. Top speed for plasmodial slime mold is about one millimeter per day.

Like the cellular slime molds, the plasmodium will change forms to create fruiting bodies when conditions deteriorate for survival. From these fruiting bodies, individual spores are created. A new plasmodial slime mold can form from a single spore when conditions improve.

| Slime mold progression

The slime mold progression image gives an example of a plasmodial slime mold species, *Fuligo septica*. The reproductive stage is called an aethalium. A mature aethalium has a protective outer covering with millions of tiny spores just under the surface. *Fuligo septica* is commonly known as "vomit slime mold." Can you see why?

| Fuligo septica

PHYLUM OOMYCOTA (WATER MOLDS)

Members of the phylum Oomycota, commonly known as water molds, are almost all found in fresh-water environments or are plant parasites. While you may never have heard of water molds before, they have had and continue to have a significant impact on our lives and even on our history. Certain aquatic water molds cause problems for individuals who make their living in aquaculture. When fish are overcrowded, they are likely to make contact with each other and cause numerous surface wounds. Certain water mold species can then infect the wound site and begin decomposing the live fish, causing them to lose their protective scales.

Another water mold holds a large place in U.S. history books. *Phytophthora infestans* is a plant parasitic water mold which can wipe out an entire crop of potatoes in a very short period of time. Have you ever read about the Irish Potato Famine? During the 1840s and 1850s, Ireland experienced the devastating effects of late blight of potatoes, caused by *Phytophthora infestans*. To escape starvation during the potato famine approximately one million people emigrated to America from Ireland, thus changing the face of America. In ten years from 1841 to 1851, the estimated population of Ireland dropped from 8 million to 6.5 million people.

Late blight of potatoes spreads most quickly during cool, wet weather. The flagellated zoospores of the water mold are able to move from leaf to leaf easily and spread the disease quickly when there are water droplets on the leaves to swim through. In a matter of a few days, an entire field can be wiped out.

Blight is also quite common in other food crops such as tomatoes, pineapple, and peppers. Farmers spend large amounts of money every year to protect our food from water molds all around the world.

Fill in the blanks.

4.25 Discuss the similarities and differences between the feeding phase of the plasmodial slime mold and the cellular slime mold. _____

_____

_____

_____

_____

_____

4.26 Why are members of phyla Acrasiomycota, Myxomycota, and Oomycota not classified in the kingdom Fungi? _____

_____

4.27 What are two types of environments that you are likely to find water molds?

_____

4.28 In plasmodial slime molds, the plasmodium transforms into a _____ , the reproductive structure.

4.29 Discuss the organism and its affects that where responsible for a large emigration from Ireland to the United States in the mid-nineteenth century. _____

_____

_____

_____

_____

_____

Review the material in this section in preparation for the Self Test. This Self Test will check your mastery of this particular section as well as your knowledge of all previous sections.

SELF TEST 4

Write the letter for the correct answer on each blank (each answer, 3 points).

4.01   Which phylum is NOT part of the kingdom Protista? _____
a. Acrasiomycota   b. Myxomycota   c. Zygomycota   d. Oomycota

4.02   Which substance is responsible for the red color in red algae? _____
a. fucoxanthin   b. carotenoids   c. phycoerythrin   d. chlorophyll

4.03   The Anopheles mosquito is the _____ for malaria.
a. insect vector   b. host   c. thallus   d. parasite

4.04   Through the process of _____ , an amoeba creates a food vacuole where digestion continues.
a. fermentation   b. chemotaxis   c. budding   d. phagocytosis

4.05   Which item is NOT associated with the phylum Rhodophyta? _____
a. red algae   b. algin   c. agar   d. carrageenan

Match these definitions (each answer, 3 points).

4.06	_____ late blight	a. light-sensitive structure
4.07	_____ sulcus	b. groove in the outer covering of dinoflagellates
4.08	_____ radiolarians	c. bright specimen on a dark background
4.09	_____ plasmodial slime mold	d. single body tube
4.010	_____ algin	e. Phytophthora infestans
4.011	_____ daughter colonies	f. multi-nucleated feeding phase
4.012	_____ monocular	g. rapid growth of algae
4.013	_____ phototaxis	h. giant brown algae
4.014	_____ red eyespot	i. gelatin-like derivative of brown algae
4.015	_____ thallus	j. result of reproduction inside a Volvox colony
4.016	_____ dark-field microscope	k. structure of an alga
4.017	_____ diatoms	l. response to light
4.018	_____ algal bloom	m. Foraminifera
4.019	_____ plasmodium	n. Myxomycota
4.020	_____ kelp	o. Bacillariophyta

Complete these items (each numbered item, 4 points).

4.021   Give three reasons that euglena have been classified as protozoans in the past.

_____

_____

4.022   List at least three reasons that diatoms are of significant importance to us.

_____

_____

4.023   The species _____ _____ is notorious off the coast of Florida

for causing severe _____ _____ when conditions are just right.

One of many possible affects these algal blooms have includes many people potentially

becoming ill from _____ _____ _____ after eating

clams that have ingested large amounts of these dinoflagellates.

4.024   Discuss malaria, one of the most heavily researched organisms in the world.
Include: the scientific genus of the microorganism; the insect vector; and at least three other
details about malaria.

_____

_____

_____

Match the scientific name with the correct phylum (each answer, 3 points).

4.025 _____ Synura

4.026 _____ Volvox

4.027 _____ Giardia lamblia

4.028 _____ Saccharomyces cerevisiae

4.029 _____ Amoeba proteus

4.030 _____ Plasmodium ovale

4.031 _____ Sargassum

4.032 _____ Agaricus bisporis

a. Basidiomycota

b. Rhizopoda

c. Zoomastigophora

d. Chlorophyta

e. Ascomycota

f. Phaeophyta

g. Chrysophyta

h. Apicomplexa

80 / 100   SCORE _____   TEACHER _____ _____
initials   date

5. EUBACTERIA

The next two kingdoms we will study in this LIFEPAC contain all organisms with a prokaryotic cells structure. Members of the kingdoms Eubacteria and Archaea are unicellular organisms with a prokaryotic cell structure which does not have a membrane-bound nucleus.

Plants, Animals, Fungi, and all Protista are composed of cells with membrane-bound organelles within the cell membrane, eukaryotic cells. Before we take a look at the kingdoms Eubacteria and Archaea, we will review some general characteristics of prokaryotic cells.

Section Objectives

Review these objectives. When you have completed this section, you should be able to:

6. Discuss what characteristics set organisms of a particular kingdom apart from members of other kingdoms.

9. Discuss the economic and environmental impact of the groups of microorganisms.

16. List and describe eubacteria based on Gram staining and shape.

17. List and describe three groups of archaea.

18. List and describe the structures and characteristics of viruses, prions, and viroids.

Vocabulary

Study these words to enhance your learning success in this section.

nucleoid	pathogen	normal flora	cyanobacteria
Gram stain	peptidoglycan	bacillus	enteric bacteria
transformation	transduction	coccus	mycobacterium
bacteriophage	spirillum	anaerobic	extremophile
rickettsia	salinity	methanogen	halophile
thermoacidophile	virologist	receptor site	viral budding
virulence	virion	inactivated vaccine	lytic cycle
attenuated vaccine	capsid	lysogenic cycle	prion
envelope	lysis	viral replication	latent infection
viroid		parasite	
opportunistic infection		bacterial conjugation	
obligate intracellular		viral attachment protein	

PROKARYOTE REVIEW

Though prokaryotic cells do not contain a true nucleus, they do contain genetic material in the form of DNA and/or RNA. This genetic material forms the **nucleoid** area of the cell, which has no membrane separating it from the rest of the cytoplasm. Prokaryote means "before nut" while the term "nut" refers to the membrane-bound nucleus. This term is the result of a faulty evolutionary world-view which states that eukaryotic species are more complicated and have evolved from prokaryotic organisms. With the help of electron microscopes, scientists continue to make discoveries about bacteria and other prokaryotes that show that they are not nearly as simple as scientists once assumed.

Sexual reproduction is only known to take place in eukaryotic organisms. For prokaryotes, all reproduction is the result of asexual binary fission. There are, however, three non-reproductive processes in which prokaryotic cells may share genetic material; **bacterial conjugation**, **transformation**, and **transduction**. In each process, genetic material from outside a prokaryotic cell is incorporated into the cell's genetic material in some way. Through bacterial conjugation, genetic material is transferred from one bacteria cell to another through direct contact with each other. Some bacterial cells are capable of taking in naked DNA or RNA from outside the cell membrane through transformation. Transduction is specialized sharing of genetic material through a parasitic organism called a **bacteriophage**. A bacteriophage is a virus that infects a bacteria cell.

EUBACTERIA (BACTERIA)

The kingdom Eubacteria includes those organisms we most often think of as bacteria. For example, this kingdom includes many **pathogens**, organisms which cause disease. In addition, this kingdom also includes many organisms that are responsible for spoiling food, as well as for flavoring food. Along with members of the kingdom Fungi, eubacteria are necessary in our ecosystems as decomposers. While there are many bacteria that cause trouble for humans, the majority of bacteria are either harmless or helpful to humans. In fact, you are surrounded by bacteria nearly everywhere you might be studying. Thousands of bacteria are living directly on and in your body at any one time.

Taxonomic classification of the thousands of identified species in the kingdom Eubacteria has changed significantly with the development of the electron microscope and with new findings in molecular biology. In the past, bacterial classification was based largely on a standard staining mechanism, the Gram stain. Classification systems have also considered the shape of the bacteria and the environment or host where the bacteria lived. Since these characteristics are still helpful in identifying bacteria, we will take a look at these bacterial characteristics; however, in this LIFEPAC text, we will not attempt to classify bacteria into specific phylum. After we have studied these characteristic properties of bacteria, we will then take a look at a number of examples of bacteria species and the diseases caused by these pathogenic bacteria.

The Gram stain. In the 1880s, Hans Christian Gram, a Danish bacteriologist, discovered and developed a method of staining bacteria for viewing under a microscope, the Gram stain. The Gram stain is actually a defined series of stains and rinses that produces predictable results. First, crystal violet is applied to a bacterial specimen. After a series of rinses, then a safranine stain is applied. The crystal violet stain will create a blue or purple color, while the safranine will create a pink color. In Gram-negative cells, the crystal violet stain is easily washed away by the rinsing procedure.

However, in a Gram-positive cell, the purple or blue crystal violet color is retained. Bacteria can then be broadly classified as either Gram-positive (purple) or Gram-negative (pink).

At the time that Hans Christian Gram developed this technique, molecular biology was not yet a developed science, and little was known as to "why" the Gram stain worked as it did. Today, we know that the molecular basis of the Gram stain has to do with a molecule present in the bacterial cell wall, peptidoglycan. Gram-positive bacteria have thick cell walls with multiple layers of peptidoglycans molecules. About 90% of the cell wall is composed these large, complex molecules. Gram-negative bacteria, on the other hand, have a single layer of peptidoglycans, thus making a thin cell wall. In Gram-negative bacteria, the cell wall includes about 20% peptidoglycans. Even today, the Gram stain is one of the first steps used to identify the species of bacteria in a laboratory.

 View 1003 Microscope: Rhizobia, from the 10th Grade SCIENCE EXPERIMENTS Video

Cell shape. While most of the classification systems microbiologists and bacteriologists use today are based on specific molecular and genetic make-ups, many of the scientific names given to bacteria give you a clue as to shape and other characteristics of the species. A rod shaped bacterium is called a bacillus. A round bacterium is called a coccus. A spiral shaped bacterium is called a spirillum. *Lactobacillus* are rod shaped bacteria that convert lactose, as well as other simple sugars, into lactic acid. Certain *Lactobacillus* species are important in the production of food such as cider, yogurt, and wine. *Streptococcus*, a group of round bacteria species which typically occur in chains, and *Staphylococcus*, round bacteria which occur in "bunches," both include many species pathogenic to humans.

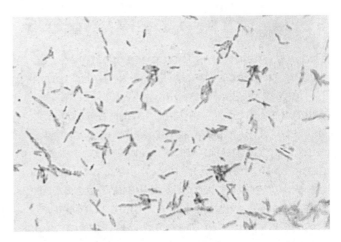

| Gram - negative

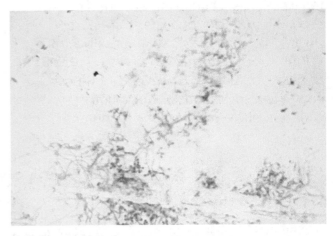

| Gram - positive

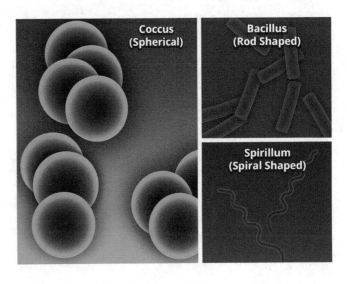

EUBACTERIA ALL AROUND US

The vast majority of the approximately 5,000 known species of bacteria are actually harmless or helpful to us. However, in this LIFEPAC, we will take a look at some common pathogenic bacteria. The following table is a very small sampling of the bacteria known to be pathogenic to humans. For this LIFEPAC, you will not be expected to memorize all the material on this table; however, you should be prepared to discuss some of the bacteria referenced as examples in the lesson text.

Gram-positive cocci. The most common bacterial pathogens of humans are Gram-positive cocci.Many species of bacteria are part of the normal flora that lives symbiotically with humans. Gram-positive cocci are no exception to this normal flora. However, Gram-positive cocci are also responsible for many of the most common bacterial infections for humans. You might ask, "If they are always present on our body, then how can they also cause so many infections and diseases?" The best answer is that many *Staphylococcus* and *Streptococcus* infections are opportunistic infections. When there is a change in the symbiotic environment which allows infectious growth or when the bacteria infect a different part of the body than where it typically lives, then an opportunistic infection may occur.

One common change in the symbiotic environment is the result of a compromised immune system. If you have ever developed strep throat after a tough battle with the common cold, then you have experienced the effects of an opportunistic *Streptococcus* infection. If you know someone who developed a staph infection right after a complicated surgery, then it may have been an opportunistic *Staphylococcus* infection.

GRAM-POSITIVE COCCI		
Disease	**Agent**	**Transmission**
Numerous Staph Infections	*Staphylococcus aureus*	Food, Direct Contact, Infected Animal
Strep Throat, Scarlet Fever, etc.	*Strphococcus pyogenes*	Direct Contact
GRAM-POSITIVE BACILLI		
Disease	**Agent**	**Transmission**
Anthrax	*Bacillus anthracis*	Soil, Infected Animal
Tetnus	*Clostridium tetani*	Soil
Botulism	*Clostridium botulinum*	Food
Diptheria	*Corynebacterium diptheriae*	Respiratory Contact
GRAM-NEGATIVE COCCI AND BACILLI		
Disease	**Agent**	**Transmission**
Gonorrhea	*Neisseria gonorrhoeae* (cocci)	Sexual Contact
Whooping Cough	*Bordetella pertussis* (bacilli)	Respiratory Contact
Gastroenteritis, UTIs	*Escherichia coli* (bacilli)	Food, Water
Typhoid Fever	*Salmonella typhi* (bacilli)	Food, Water
Bubonic Plague	*Yersina pestis* (bacilli)	Insect Vector (flea)
Cholera	*Vibrio cholerae* (vibrio)	Water
Stomach Ulcers	*Helicobacter pylori* (vibrio)	Unknown

SPIROCHETES AND MYCOBACTERIUM

Disease	Agent	Transmission
Syphilis	*Treponema pallidum* (spirochete)	Sexual Contact
Lyme disease	*Borrelia bugdorferi* (spirochete)	Insect Vector (tick)
Tuberculosis (TB)	*Mycobacterium tuberculosis* (mycobacterium)	Respiratory Contact
Leprosy	*Mycobacterium lepae* (mycobacterium)	Direct Contact

CHLAMYDIAE AND RICKETTSIAS

Disease	Agent	Transmission
Chlamydia	*Chlamydia trachomatis* (clamidiae)	Sexual Contact
Typhus	*Rickettsia prawazekii*	Insect Vector (lice)
Rocky Mountain Spotted Fever	*Rickettsia rickettsii*	Insect Vector (tick)

BACTERIAL PNEUMONIA AGENTS

Disease	Agent	Transmission
Pneumonia	*Streptococcus pneumoniae* (G+ cocci)	Respiratory Contact
Pneumonia	*Haemophilus influenzae* (G- bacilli)	Respiratory Contact
Pneumonia	*Chlamydia pneumoniae* (clamidiae)	Respiratory Contact
Pneumonia	*Mycoplasma pneumoniae* (mycoplasma)	Respiratory Contact

Gram-negative bacilli. *Escherichia coli*, as well as many other Gram-negative bacilli, are members of a group called enteric bacteria. Enteric bacteria commonly live in the intestine of humans and other animals, as well as in soil and water. Most of the time, *E. coli* lives in a symbiotic relationship with its host, however, opportunistic infections of E. coli are common when the bacteria is inadvertently introduced to areas of the body where it does not normally live, such as the urinary tract. Also, there are many different strains of E. coli that are much more pathogenic than most. One such strain *E coli* O157:H7 is known to be one of the most virulent strains world-wide.

Spirochetes. Another group of bacteria known as spirochetes are made up of Gram-negative spirillum bacteria. An example of a spirochete is *Borrelia burgdorferi*, the bacteria which causes Lyme disease. In North America, *Borrelia burgdorferi* is carried by a deer tick vector which transmits Lyme disease through a tick bite. Common symptoms of Lyme disease include a bulls-eye shaped rash around the site where the tick bite occurred, fever, and general muscle aches. The picture shows a typical bulls-eye shaped rash around a tick bite location. Chronic symptoms may include neurological problems and heart problems.

Mycobacterium. Tuberculosis (TB) is a serious respiratory disease caused by bacteria with a "waxy" cell wall, a mycobacterium. *Mycobacterium tuberculosis* spreads easily through the air when a person with tuberculosis coughs, sneezes, or simply talks. World-wide, nearly 2 million people die each year from TB. Almost one third of the world's population is estimated to be infected with TB; however, many of those infected may develop TB much later when their immune system is compromised, or may potentially never develop the disease. Cases of virulent TB are a big concern right now because of the enormous number of people in the world with depressed immune systems because of HIV/AIDS infections.

Rickettsia. Typhus fever is caused by tiny bacteria known as rickettsias. Rickettsias are obligate intracellular parasites; which means that they can not live outside a host cell. *Rickettsia prawazekii*, the bacterial cause of typhus fever, is transferred from human to human by a specific insect vector, a human body louse. Typhus fever is most common where overcrowding and poor hygiene create ideal living conditions in the bedding and clothing for body lice. Controlling this insect vector is the key to controlling this disease.

Cyanobacteria. Unlike the other examples we have explored thus far, cyanobacteria is not usually a pathogenic bacteria; however, some unique characteristics lead us to take a brief look at this group of bacteria. Because of the presence of chlorophyll, cyanobacteria used to be classified as a type of algae. In fact, cyanobacteria are still commonly referred to as blue-green algae. Cyanobacteria are photosynthetic bacteria that must live in aquatic environments. Like other true algae, when conditions are nearly perfect, cyanobacteria may

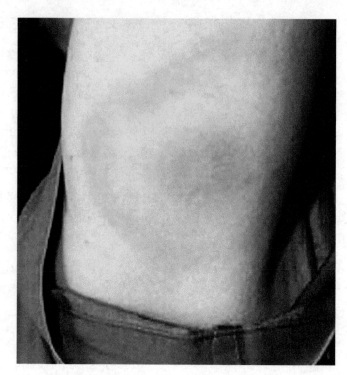

| Lyme disease tick bite location

grow rapidly to cause a bloom. Certain other species of cyanobacteria are important to many crops around the world because of their ability to convert elemental nitrogen into nitrogen sources which plants can use.

 LEARNING APPLICATION: Pathogenic bacteria report.

Write a 600-1000 word research report on a pathogenic bacterium that is not discussed in this LIFEPAC text. (You may choose one from the table.) Include history, the scientific name of the bacterium, vectors, symptoms, etc.

TEACHER CHECK _____ _____
                                              initials   date

Write the answers on the blanks.

5.1 Explain the general differences between eukaryotic cells and prokaryotic cells.

_____

_____

5.2 Discuss where the term "prokaryote" came from. Discuss the problem with this premise.

_____

_____

_____

5.3 Briefly describe each means of sharing genetic material in bacteria.

a. bacterial conjugation _____

b. transformation _____

c. transduction _____

5.4 List several affects of bacteria on the world around us other than as pathogens.

_____

_____

5.5 The molecular basis of the Gram stain is the amount of _____ in the bacterial cell wall.

5.6 Describe the cell wall of a Gram-negative bacterium. _____

_____

5.7 What shape of cell is each given bacterium?

a. Lactobacillus _____

b. Streptococcus _____

c. Spirochetes _____

5.8 Give the scientific name of the bacteria responsible for each condition.

a. Typhus fever _____

b. Diarrhea, Gastroenteritis, UTIs _____

c. Strep Throat, Tonsillitis _____

d. Tuberculosis _____

e. Lyme disease _____

f. Staph infections, Toxic Shock Syndrome _____

5.9 Define each term.

a. normal flora _____

b. opportunistic infection _____

c. obligate intracellular parasite _____

d. blue-green algae _____

ARCHAEA

Archaea live in some of the most extreme environments on earth. In fact, many of the species within this kingdom live in places where scientists once believed the conditions to be so harsh that there could not possibly be any living things found there. The Dead Sea, found between Jordan and Israel, was named accordingly thousands of years ago because no fish or plants live in its super-salty waters. Scientists know today that the Dead Sea really does have living organisms thriving in it, certain species of archaea, commonly known as halophiles. Archaea are sometimes called extremophiles because of these extreme environments.

| Dead Sea

The prokaryotic cell structure of archaea differs from eubacteria in some important ways. In fact, the cell structure of archaea shares some similarities with eukaryotic cells as well as with the prokaryotic eubacteria cells. While archaea cells are prokaryotic, the structure of the genetic material in archaea cells is more similar to the DNA structure of the eukaryotic cells. Another way in which archaea cells differ from eubacteria cells is in the structure of the cell membrane and cell wall. The outer structure of archaea does not include a layer of peptidoglycans like eubacteria cells.

Since the taxonomic structure of archaea, like that of eubacteria, is in such a state of fluctuation, we will not focus on any particular system of phyla or divisions. However, we will take a look at three common groups of archaea based on the environments where the species live. These groups are methanogens, halophiles, and thermoacidophiles.

METHANOGENS

Methanogens live in anaerobic environments such as in swamp sludge, sewer sludge, and the gut of many animals. Anaerobic organisms, such as methanogens, do not require oxygen to live. In fact, many anaerobic organisms can not survive in the presence of free oxygen.

The word methanogen means "methane producing." Methane gas is produced by methanogens as the product of their respiration cycle. This methane gas is often called "swamp gas" or "marsh gas" in swampy locations. This same methane gas produced by archaea living in the intestines is the cause of flatulence in humans and other animals.

HALOPHILES

Halophiles are archaea which live in high **salinity** water such as the Dead Sea already mentioned above. Salinity is the concentration of salt in a body of water. For comparison purposes, the earth's oceans average about 3.5% salinity; the Dead Sea salinity levels are between 30% and 35% and a saturated solution of salt is about 36% - 37% salinity. Halophiles have a unique system that keeps the inside structure of the cell at a salinity level similar to the environment the unicellular organism lives in. Various species of the halophiles which live in the Dead Sea are responsible for some of the bright colors found there along the shores.

| Owens Lake

The dried lake bed of Owens Lake in the Mojave Desert of California is another location where carotenoids-producing halophiles thrive. In the summer, when ground temperatures reach well over 100°C and the shallow pools of water evaporate, the concentration of halophiles can be high enough to create the deep red colors seen in the photo. During these summer months, some of these areas where water remains become 100% saturated with salt. Now that's extreme living!

THERMOACIDOPHILES

Thermoacidophiles thrive in high temperature and/or highly acidic environments, often well beyond levels where most organisms could survive. Some species of thermoacidophiles grow in temperatures up to 115°C—that's 15 degrees above the boiling point of water. Other species can tolerate acidic environments with pH levels as low as 2; the strongest acids have a pH level of 1.

One example of a thermoacidophile that was first isolated in 1982 is an adversary of the fruit-juice processing industry. This tiny organism, called *Alicyclobacillus*, is responsible for spoiling many fruit juices, even after precautions have been taken in the production process to pasteurize the juices. Alicyclobacillus spores can tolerate the heating process many producers use for pasteurization. In addition to this characteristic, *Alicyclobacillus* grows very well at low pH levels like those found in apple juice, pear juice, orange juice, and tomato juice.

Another example of a thermoacidophile, *Sulfolobus acidocaldarius*, was discovered growing in the hot sulfur springs of Yellowstone National Park by Thomas D. Brock. This thermoacidophile grows in an optimal temperature range of about 80-90°C; however, it can withstand temperatures up to 115°C. The boiling point of water at Yellowstone is about 92°C! *Sulfolobus acidocaldarius* is able to use elemental sulfur in its respiration cycle, producing sulfuric acid.

| Mammoth Hot Springs, Yellowstone Park

Fill in the blanks.

5.10 Explain why members of the kingdom Archaea are often called extremophiles?

_____

5.11 What does anaerobic mean? _____

5.12 Describe the extreme conditions each group of archaea are known to live in.

    a. Methanogens _____

    b. Halophiles _____

    c. Thermoacidophiles _____

5.13 What is the scientific name of the organism responsible for souring fruit juice that is mentioned in the text? What group does this organism belong? _____

_____

VIRUSES, PRIONS, AND VIROIDS

Most of us are familiar with the effects of certain viruses on our bodies. The common cold, influenza, chicken pox, cold sores, and warts are all the result of a viral infection. Viruses, as well as prions and viroids, offer scientists a unique challenge in classification. Although scientists have substantial data showing the ill effects that viruses, prions, and viroids have on living organisms, many **virologists** do not consider these structures as living organisms. Three reasons these structures are not considered living organisms include:

1. They are not able to reproduce independently.

2. They do not use energy for metabolism of any kind.

3. Crystalline (non-living) cultures of viruses, prions, and viroids can theoretically be produced and kept indefinitely in storage while still maintaining the virulence of the culture.

Virulence is the ability of a virus to cause disease. When the crystalline culture is introduced to a potential living host cell, infection will follow. All other pathogenic organisms we have studied must be living in order to cause infection in a plant or animal. We will discuss these points more thoroughly in this section of the LIFEPAC.

VIRUSES

Structure. The simple structure of a single virus unit is called the **virion**. Each virion is composed of two parts: genetic material in the form of DNA or RNA, and a protein coating surrounding the genetic material called a **capsid**. The structure of some virions also includes an **envelope** made primarily of lipids.

The genetic material in a virion is composed of nucleic acid molecules in the form of either DNA (deoxyribonucleic acid) or RNA (ribonucleic acid), but never both. Often, viruses are classified by the type and structure of the genetic material. For example, the genetic material may be single-stranded DNA, double-stranded DNA, single-stranded RNA, or double-stranded RNA. (Genetic material in humans is always composed of double-stranded DNA.)

The capsid produces the outward shape of the virion while enclosing the genetic material. The shape and structure of this protein covering is another way to group viruses. Some common shapes are icosahedral, helical, and complex. The following images are representatives of each shape. An icosahedral virus almost appears spherical like a ball; however, it is actually made up of twenty identical sides. Many types of viruses which are responsible for the common cold, as well as the virus responsible for HIV/AIDS, have an icosahedral shape.

An example of a helical virus is the Tobacco Mosaic Virus (TMV). The genetic material in this virus is shaped like a stretched spring. The TMV capsid forms a rod-shaped exterior to the virion. The TMV Helical Virus illustration is of a complex-shaped virion.

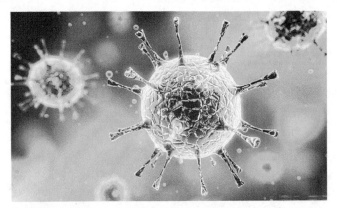

| Germ virus

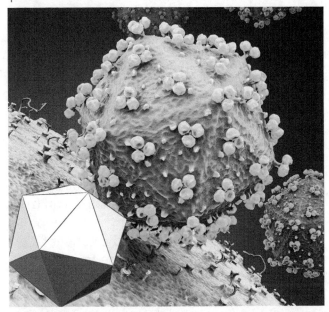

| HIV Icosahedral virus

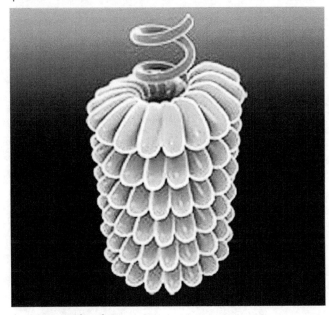

| TMV Helical virus

| T4 bacteriophage complex virus

In the case of the T4 bacteriophage, the protein capsid has a very distinctive shape with the various components serving specific functions in how this virus interacts with its bacterial host cell.

The envelope is an outside lipid-based layer surrounding some virions. In almost all cases, only viruses that live in very specialized animal host cells include an envelope. The envelope is not actually a structure that the genetic material in a virion is able to code for; instead, the envelope is made up of material obtained directly from the host cell membrane when the virion leaves the host cell.

Since all viruses are very specific about what kind of cell they are able to infect, the type of host is also a common means of classifying viruses. The T4 bacteriophage is a specific virus which infects only E. coli bacteria. A bacteriophage is a virus which must infect a bacterium to replicate. Other viruses are classified based on what kind of plant or animal cell acts as the host cell for the virus.

Viral replication cycle. Although viruses are not capable of reproduction in the same sense as all other cells we have discussed, as obligate intracellular parasites, their ability to create new viruses often seems almost inexhaustible. Since each virion does not include any "machinery" necessary for reproduction, the virus depends completely on "hi-jacking" the internal machinery of their host cells. In this way, **viral replication** of viruses is commonly described as a "manufacturing and assembly" process. We will study this unique process in five steps: attachment, penetration, uncoating, replication, and release.

The following diagram is a simplified representation of the lytic cycle of the T4 bacteriophage. (a) attachment; (b) penetration; (no uncoating is necessary here); (c) and (d) replication (manufacturing and assembly); (e) release (cell lysis)

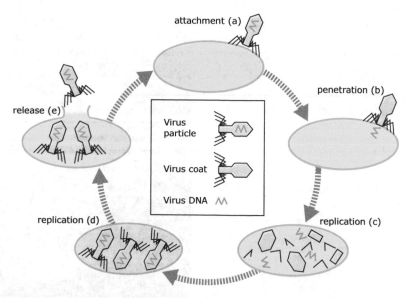

| Lytic viral replication cycle – Bacteriophage

a. Attachment. The first step in the cycle involves the virus actually coming into contact with the correct type of host cell and attaching itself to the cell wall or cell membrane of that host cell. This is accomplished by the matching up of specialized structures on both the virion and the host cell. If the receptor site on the host cell does not match perfectly with the viral attachment protein of the virion, the virion will not attach to the cell and infection will not take place. The receptor site may be any number of structures on the outside of a potential host cell that is very specific to that type of a cell. The viral attachment protein is part of the protein capsid of a virion. This mechanism is what keeps the common cold virus, which will only infect the cells of the respiratory tract, from infecting our blood cells, our bone cells, or the cells of our nervous system.

b. Penetration. Once a virion has attached itself to the outside of a cell, the next step in the cycle is getting inside the host cell. In order for the virion to take over the host cell's "machinery," it is necessary to get the genetic material of the virion inside the host cell. This may happen a number of different ways. For example, the T4 bacteriophage injects only the DNA genetic material into the E. coli cell while the capsid remains outside the host cell. In other cases, the entire virion, including the capsid, enters the cell in a manner similar to phagocytosis in *amoeba proteus*.

c. Uncoating. Once inside the host cell, the viral genetic material must get into place within the host cell where it will be used to dictate the "manufacturing and assembly" functions of the host cell "machinery." In some cases, the capsid is removed completely and the genetic material either remains in the host cell cytoplasm or the genetic material makes its way into the host cell nucleus where it may join the host cell genetic material. In other cases, the capsid is only partially removed and the new "command center" is set up in the region of the host cell where the viral genetic material and modified capsid remain.

d. Replication. This next step in the viral replication cycle is when the "manufacturing and assembly" actually take place. During the replication step in a lytic cycle, the "hi-jacked" host cell structures create new copies of the viral genetic material and new proteins which will become the viral capsid. The viral parts are then put together within the cell to form new virions which will be released during the release step in the viral replication cycle.

At this point in the replication cycle, there are some viruses that may simply cause their genetic material to join the genetic material of the host cell, but not immediately begin the manufacture of new material for new virions. These viruses enter what is called a lysogenic cycle. During this cycle, a viral infection is often referred to as a latent infection. No cells are being destroyed; thus the typical symptoms of infection are lacking in the host organism. However, because the viral genetic material has been incorporated into the host cell genetic material, as the host cell grows and reproduces, the new daughter cells also contain the viral genetic material and viral replication continues.

e. Release. If a virus has caused a latent infection, then this final step in a viral replication cycle is postponed indefinitely until some outside stimulant causes the virus to enter a lytic cycle. In the case of a viral infection already in a lytic cycle, this step typically ends with the death of the host cell and the release of the replicated virions.

The release of the newly assembled virions may take place through a number of different processes. Two of the most basic and common processes are cell lysis and budding. During cell lysis, the host cell simply breaks apart, releasing all cell contents, including the new virions. This common mechanism of releasing these new virions is not used when the virion includes an envelope; instead, enveloped virions are typically released through viral budding. During budding in the viral replication cycle, an envelope is formed around the viral capsid using lipids from the host cell membrane. Repeating this process over and over often leaves the host cell damaged enough that in time it will rupture or die.

History and control of viral disease. The table of human viral diseases lists some of the most common diseases caused by viruses both in the past and currently. Now, early in the twenty-first century, diseases such as AIDS, SARS, and West Nile Fever are recognized threats all over the world. Other diseases, such as polio, measles, and smallpox are considered historical diseases due to effective use of vaccinations.

Dr. Edward Jenner, an English physician, is credited with giving the first vaccination in 1796. That year, during a severe smallpox epidemic, Jenner observed that almost all people who lived in the country, especially those who had contact with milk cows, appeared to be immune to smallpox. Through his study of this phenomenon, he found that those who appeared to be immune to smallpox had previously experienced a mild ailment known as cowpox. To test his theory, Jenner purposefully exposed a young boy to cowpox. After the site of the boy's cowpox infection healed, Jenner took the boy with him to visit smallpox patients, and the boy never got smallpox. Jenner discovered that immunity to a potentially deadly disease could be artificially stimulated by purposefully infecting a person with a similar, much less serious disease.

Common Viral Diseases	Host	Genetic Structure	Capsid	Envelope
Measles	Epithelial cells (internal and external)	1s RNA	filamentous or spherical	yes
HIV/AIDS	Immune system cells	1s RNA	icosahedral (retrovirus)	yes
Ebola	Lining of blood vessels	1s RNA	filamentous	yes
Hepatitis A	Liver cells	1s RNA	icosahedral	no
Hepatitis B	Liver cells	2s DNA	icosahedral	yes
Hepatitis C	Liver cells	1s RNA	icosahedral	yes
Polio	Nervous system	1s RNA	icosahedral	no
Herpes (Cold Sores)	Nervous system	2s DNA	icosahedral	yes
West Nile Fever	Nervous system	1s RNA	icosahedral	yes
Rabies	Nervous system	1s RNA	helical	yes
Chickenpox/ Shingles	Nervous system	2s DNA	spherical	yes
Smallpox	Small blood vessels of skin, mouth, and throat	2s DNA	large brick-shaped	both
Common Cold (Picornavirus)	Upper respiratory	1s RNA	icosahedral	no
Common Cold (Coronavirus)	Upper respiratory	1s RNA	helical	yes
Influenza	Upper respiratory	1s RNA	spherical or filamentous	yes
SARS	Upper respiratory, lower respiratory, and GI	1s RNA	helical	yes

In the case of smallpox, thanks to the collaborative vaccination efforts of the World Health Organization in the 1960s, smallpox has been completely wiped out. The last reported case of smallpox was in 1978; thus, regular vaccinations for smallpox are no longer necessary. Other diseases, such as measles and polio, are also easily avoided where vaccinations are commonly practiced.

Today we know much more about how vaccinations work than when Jenner studied smallpox. A vaccination is given in order to stimulate the human immune system to create antibodies to fight a disease. As long as these antibodies remain in the human body, a level of immunity is maintained. This immune response is commonly achieved using either an inactivated vaccine or an attenuated vaccine. An **inactivated vaccine** is made from a virus that has been altered to the point that it could no longer infect a cell; however, the immune system is able to recognize the material as a virus and create antibodies. An **attenuated vaccine** is made from actual "live" viruses that are capable of infecting cells, but are capable of replication only at very slow rates, thus allowing the immune system to keep them from causing disease symptoms.

PRIONS AND VIROIDS

Prions and viroids, along with viruses, are capable of causing diseases but do not meet most scientists' definition of living organisms. Unlike viruses, which are composed of two different kinds of materials, nucleic acids(genetic material) and proteins(capsids), prions and viroids are composed of one type of material only.

Prions are abnormal protein molecules which cause disease. All known diseases caused by prions affect the brain of the host and are fatal. The following table shows some neurological diseases that are caused by these complex protein molecules. Scientists are concerned about the possibility of the transmission of these diseases from animals to humans if the meat from infected animals is eaten; however, at this time, there is little scientific evidence to support this concern. Until further research can be done, precautions have been taken worldwide to limit human exposure to the meat of infected animals.

PRION DISEASES
Animal Prion Diseases
Bovine Spongiform Encephalopathy (BSE): also known as mad cow disease
Scrapie: in sheep and goats
Feline Spongiform Encephalopathy: in cats
Transmissible Mink Encephalopathy (TME): found in domestic mink in mink ranches
Chronic Wasting Disease (CWD): in mule deer, white-tailed deer, moose, and elk
Ungulate Spongiform Encephalopathy: similar to BSE: has occurred in zoo animals in the UK
Human Prion Diseases
Creutzfeldt-Jakob Disease (CJD): a rare 1-in-a-million disease that occurs spontaneously with 10% to 15% inheritance
Variant CJD: may be related to BSE
Kuru: a brain damaging "laughing disease" found in Papua New Guinea

PRION DISEASES

Human Prion Diseases (continued)

Gerstmann-Straussler-Scheinker Syndrome (GSS): a hereditary disease which surfaces mainly in midlife

Fatal Familial Insomnia (FFI): a strange, inherited disease through which people actually die from not being able to fall asleep; surfaces later in life

Alpers Syndrome: prion disease in infants

Viroids are naked disease-causing RNA molecules. Almost all known viroids cause plant diseases, however, Hepatitis D in humans has recently been attributed to a viroid. The first viroid was discovered in 1971 by T.O. Diener, an American plant pathologist. His study of viroids was done as the result of investigating the cause of potato spindle tuber disease. In humans, Hepatitis D has been attributed to a unique viroid that relies on the Hepatitis B virus to infect a human liver cell. Thus, in order for a person to suffer from Hepatitis D, he must also have Hepatitis B at the same time. The discovery of prion and viroid diseases is relatively new; thus, new research and information about how they work is becoming available all the time.

 Fill in the blanks.

5.14 List three reasons that viruses, prions, and viroids are not classified as living organisms.

1. _____

2. _____

3. _____

5.15 Define the following structures.

virion _____

viral genetic material _____

capsid _____

envelope _____

5.16 Give three common shapes of viruses and an example of each. _____

_____

5.17 Describe the viral replication cycle. Be sure to discuss the difference between a lytic cycle

and alysogenic cycle. _____

_____

_____

_____

5.18 What is the difference between an inactivated vaccine and an attenuated vaccine? _____

_____

_____

5.19 What is a prion and what kinds of diseases are caused by prions? _____

_____

_____

5.20 What is a viroid and what kinds of diseases are caused by viroids? _____

_____

_____

Before you take this last Self Test, you may want to do one or more of these self checks.

1. _____ Read the objectives. See if you can do them.
2. _____ Restudy the material related to any objectives that you cannot do.
3. _____ Use the **SQ3R** study procedure to review the material:
    a. **S**can the sections.
    b. **Q**uestion yourself.
    c. **R**ead to answer your questions.
    d. **R**ecite the answers to yourself.
    e. **R**eview areas you did not understand.
4. _____ Review all vocabulary, activities, and Self Tests, writing a correct answer for every
    wrong answer.

SELF TEST 5

Match these words and phrases (each answer, 2 points).

5.01 _____ organisms in which a parasite lives

5.02 _____ microorganisms commonly found living in or on a human

5.03 _____ area of prokaryotic cell that is dense with genetic material

5.04 _____ structure of an alga

5.05 _____ pathogenic abnormal protein structure

5.06 _____ without free oxygen

5.07 _____ rupturing of a cell

5.08 _____ concentration of salt in water

5.09 _____ organism which causes disease

5.010 _____ obtain food from dead organic material

5.011 _____ pathogenic RNA molecule

5.012 _____ mutually positive relationship

5.013 _____ organism which lives in or on another organism

5.014 _____ the study of algae

5.015 _____ scientist who studies viruses

5.016 _____ single virus unit

a. nucleoid
b. pathogen
c. normal flora
d. anaerobic
e. salinity
f. virologist
g. phycology
h. virion
i. prion
j. viroid
k. thallus
l. lysis
m. parasite
n. saprophyte
o. symbiosis
p. host

Complete each sentence (each answer, 2 points).

5.017 Bacteria share genetic material through the processes called _____ , _____ , and _____ .

5.018 _____ is the material found in the bacterial cell wall that forms the molecular basis of the Gram stain.

5.019 _____ are spherical bacteria; _____ are rod-shaped bacteria; and _____ are spring-shaped bacteria.

5.020 During a _____ infection by a virus, viral replication is continuing but cells are not rupturing in the _____ cycle.

5.021 A virion is able to recognize the correct host cell when the _____ of the virion and the _____ of the host cell match up.

5.022 Rickettsia and viruses are examples of _____ which can only replicate inside a host cell.

5.023 Bacteria which are part if the normal flora may cause disease when the immune system is compromised. This ailment is called an _____ .

5.024 Viruses which typically have a lipid covering called an _____ are released from the host cell through _____ .

Write the letter for the correct answer on each blank (each answer, 3 points).

5.025 _____ is a group of bacteria that used to be classified as algae.
a. mycobacteria   b. cyanobacteria   c. rickettsias   d. dinoflagellates

5.026 The earth's oceans have a salinity of approximately 3.5% while the Dead Sea has a salinity of approximately _____ .
a. 30% - 35%   b. 85% - 90%   c. 36% - 37%   d. 13% - 20 %

5.027 Thermoacidophiles thrive in _____ environments.
a. salty   b. cold   c. anaerobic   d. hot, acidic

5.028 _____ is composed of large deposits of the silicon exoskeletons of members of the phylum Bacillariophyta.
a. Carrageenan   b. Lichens
c. Diatomaceous earth   d. Red tide

5.029 _____ is caused by four known Plasmodium species which rely on a mosquito insect vector.
a. African sleeping sickness   b. Lyme disease
c. Malaria   d. Hepatitis

5.030 All known diseases caused by prions affect the _____ of the host organism.
a. nervous system   b. respiratory system   c. skin   d. liver

5.031 The thread-like structures which are the building blocks of fungi are called _____ .
a. fruiting bodies   b. hyphae   c. zygosporangium   d. thallus

5.032 One of the limitations of the light microscope is the _____ .
a. long specimen preparation   b. extreme expense
c. inability to watch live processes   d. resolving power

Complete these activities.

5.033 List and describe the steps of a lytic viral replication cycle. (10 points)

a. _____

_____

b. _____

_____

c. _____

_____

d. _____

_____

e. _____

_____

5.034 Describe the Gram stain process and explain the predicted outcome of a Gram-positive bacteria culture and a Gram-negative culture. (4 points)

_____

_____

_____

$\frac{80}{100}$ SCORE _____ TEACHER _____ _____

initials   date

Before taking the LIFEPAC Test, you may want to do one or more of these self checks.

1. _____ Read the objectives. Check to see it you can do them.
2. _____ Restudy the material related to any objectives that you cannot do.
3. _____ Use the SQ3R study procedure to review the material.
4. _____ Review activities, Self Tests, and LIFEPAC vocabulary words.
5. _____ Restudy areas of weakness indicated by the last Self Test.

GLOSSARY

Actinopoda .... phylum of amoeboid protozoans which have a tiny shell-like structure composed of calcium carbonate

aethalium .... spore-bearing structure of plasmodial slime mold

agar .... gelatinous substance derived from red algae used by scientists as food for growing bacteria in the laboratory

algal bloom .... rapid extensive growth of algae as the result of nearly perfect growing conditions

algin .... gelatinous substance derived from brown algae used in the food industry as a thickener, stabilizer, and emulsifier

amoeboid movement .... movement by altering the consistency of cytoplasm so it flows to create pseudopodia

anaerobic .... absence of free atmospheric oxygen

anal pore .... structure of a paramecium where undigested food is eliminated from the cell

Animalia .... kingdom which contains multicellular eukaryotic organisms commonly known as animals

apical complex .... cell structure found only in parasitic species of the phylum Apicomplexa; important for interaction with and entry into host cells

Apicomplexa .... phylum of parasitic spore forming protozoans which are not motile during most of their life cycle

Archaea .... kingdom of prokaryotic unicellular organisms known for living in environments which all other organisms are unable to survive in

Ascomycota .... phylum(or division) of fungi commonly known as "sac fungi" which includes morels and yeasts

ascus .... spore-bearing structure or fruiting body of fungi of the kingdom Ascomycota; the ascus is sac-shaped

attenuated vaccine .... vaccine containing live pathogens which have been modified to make them much less virulent or non-virulent

bacillus (pl. bacilli) .... rod-shaped bacteria

bacterial conjugation .... transfer of genetic material between two bacteria through direct cell to cell contact; is not sexual reproduction like in eukaryotes

bacteriophage .... virus which infects a bacterium

Basidiomycota .... phylum(or division) of fungi commonly known as "club fungi" which includes mushrooms, toadstools, puffballs, bracket fungi, rusts, and smuts

binary fission .... asexual reproduction in which the parent organism divides to form two daughter cells

binocular .... having two body tubes with corresponding eye pieces (bi=two, ocular=eye)

body tube .... tube-like part of the microscope between the eyepiece and the objective

bright-field microscope .... microscope which creates a magnified image against a bright background; most common variation of the light (optical) microscope

brown algae .... common name of plant-like protists which are phaeophytes. Mostly composed of multicellular algae with a characteristic brown color

budding .... asexual reproduction in which a new organism develops from a portion of the parent cell that has pinched off

cap .... mushroom's fruiting body; umbrella-shaped top of a mushroom

capsid .... protein covering of a virus

carrageenan .... gelatinous extract from red algae that is used as a thickener and stabilizer in the food industry

cell .... basic unit of structure and function of a living organism

cellular slime mold .... common name of protists which are species of the phylum Acrasiomycota

chemotaxis .... organism's response to the presence of chemicals in its surroundings

chitin .... main molecular component of the cell wall of fungi and the exoskeleton of some animals

Chytridiomycota .... phylum of aquatic fungi commonly called chytrids; characterized by flagellated reproductive cells

cilia (sing. cilium) .... hair-like structures on the external surface of some microorganisms which are used for motility and feeding

Ciliophora .... phylum of protozoans with hair-like structures called cilia; species in this phylum are commonly known as ciliates

club fungi .... common name of basidiomycetes; characterized by club-shaped fruiting bodies

coccus (pl. cocci) .... spherical bacteria

compound microscope .... microscope which uses two or more lenses to create a magnified image

conjugation .... sexual reproduction in which two microorganisms unite temporarily to exchange nuclear material and ending with four new daughter cells containing the new genetic combination

contractile vacuole .... membrane-bound compartment in a unicellular organism which regulates the water and waste levels inside the cell by excreting excess water and wastes

cover slip .... small, thin sheet of glass placed over a specimen on a microscope slide to create a barrier between the specimen and the objective; also helps to flatten the specimen to a consistent thickness before viewing

cyanobacteria .... common name of a group of eubacteria which are capable of photosynthesis; this group is also commonly called blue-green algae, though they are not true algae

cyst .... protective capsule produced and occupied by some microorganisms during unfavorable conditions of the environment

cytoplasm .... all the material inside a cell membrane except the nucleus

cytoplasmic bridge .... temporary thin strand of cytoplasm connecting two microorganisms during conjugation; genetic material may be passed between the cells through this structure

daughter colonies .... in the species Volvox, the new colonies growing inside an older colony; when the older parent colony ruptures, the daughter colonies are released

depression slide .... microscope slides with an indentation in the middle to hold a drop of water or more liquid

diatomaceous earth .... deposits of the fossilized remains of diatoms

diatoms .... common name of plant-like protists which are species of the phylum Bacillariophyta; characterized by a silicon-based symmetrical exoskeleton

dinoflagellates .... common name of plant-like protists which are species of the phylum Pyrrophyta; characterized by having two flagella of two different lengths

dry-mount .... specimen prepared for viewing on a microscope slide without the use of water or another liquid

electron microscope .... microscope that uses beams of electrons instead of beams of light to create a magnified image

enteric bacteria .... bacteria which commonly live in the intestines of animals

envelope .... lipid-based membrane which encloses some viruses; made of material taken from the host cell membrane

Eubacteria .... kingdom of prokaryotic organisms which are commonly known as bacteria

euglena .... common name of plant-like protists which are species of the phylum Euglenophyta; characterized by presence of flagellum

euglenoid movement .... worm-like movement accomplished by expanding and contracting the entire cell

eukaryote .... single-celled or multicellular organism whose cells include a true membrane-bound nucleus and various other membrane-bound organelles

extremophile .... common name of species of kingdom Archaea

feeding phase .... life cycle phase of slime mold when feeding and growth are taking place

fermentation .... breakdown of complex molecules into simpler ones by a living organism

flagellum .... long, whip-like structure used by certain microorganisms for locomotion

food vacuole .... membrane-bound compartment in a unicellular organism in which food particles are digested by enzymes

Foraminifera .... phylum of amoeboid protozoans which have a tiny shell-like structure composed of silicon; they are commonly called radiolarians

fruiting bodies .... spore-producing reproductive structures of fungi

fucoxanthin .... brown-colored pigment found in some algae

Fungi (sing. fungus) .... kingdom of eukaryotic plant-like organisms which contain no tissue differentiation and no chlorophyll

gills .... spore-producing reproductive structures of a mushroom typically found on the underside of the cap

golden-brown algae .... common name of plant-like protists which are species of the phylum Chrysophyta; characteristic color is the result of the blend of green and red pigments

Gram stain .... method of staining bacteria for classification purposes; most eubacteria can be classified as either Gram-positive or Gram-negative

green algae .... common name of plant-like protists which are species of the phylum Chlorophyta; most species are various shades of green due to the presence of chlorophyll

gullet .... deepest part of the oral groove where food vacuoles are formed around a food particle

halophile .... Archaea which live in high salinity environments

homeostasis .... self-regulating exchange of water, dissolved materials, and dissolved gases between a cell and its surroundings

host .... organism in or on which a parasite lives

hyphae (sing. hypha) .... thread-like structures which together form the mycelia of fungi

inactivated vaccine .... vaccine containing non-living pathogens or parts of pathogens which the immune system will recognize and form antibodies against the pathogenic organism

kelp .... common name for large multicellular species of the phylum Phaeophyta which typically attach themselves to the floor of the sea

kelp forest .... undersea ecosystem similar in complexity to terrestrial forests

late blight .... devastating plant disease caused by Phytophthora infestans, a member of the phylum Oomycota

latent infection .... inactive infection which is still capable of becoming active and producing symptoms; often associated with the lysogenic cycle of a viral infection

lichens .... symbiotic structure between a fungi and an alga, or a fungi and a cyanobacteria

light (optical) microscope .... microscope which focuses visible light through a series of lenses to create a magnified image

longitudinal binary fission .... asexual reproduction in which the parent organism divides lengthwise to form two daughter cells which are mirror images of each other

lysis .... death of a cell by breaking the cell open

lysogenic cycle .... replication cycle of a virus in which the viral genetic material is being replicated along with the host cell genetic material, however, no new virions are being produced; an infection in the lysogenic cycle is called a latent infection

lytic cycle .... replication cycle of a virus which new virions are manufactured and assembled; end of a lytic cycle is the lysis of the host cell and the release of the new virions; disease symptoms are typically present

methanogen .... Archaea which live in an anaerobic environment and which produce methane as part of their respiratory process

microorganisms .... living organisms too small to see without the aid of a microscope

microscope slide .... thin sheet of glass used to hold specimens for observation using a microscope

monocular .... having one body tube with a single corresponding eye piece

morels .... multicellular species of the phylum Ascomycota which are also known as sponge mushrooms, although they are not true mushrooms

motile .... able to move independently

multi-nucleated .... cell structure with more than one nucleus

mycelia (sing. mycelium) .... group of hyphae which perform a specific function in a fungus

mycobacterium .... type of eubacteria with a waxy cell wall

normal flora .... microorganisms commonly found living in or on a human with no detrimental effects

nucleoid .... area of prokaryotic cell that is dense with genetic material

objective lens .... magnifying lens closest to the specimen; lower of two lenses on a compound microscope

obligate intracellular parasite .... parasitic organism which is not able to reproduce outside a host cell

ocular lens .... magnifying lens in the eyepiece of a microscope

opportunistic infection .... infection of an organism that may always be present, but is able to cause infection only as a result of a change in the normal environment

oral groove .... indentation of the pellicle of a Paramecium that opens to the gullet

pathogen .... agent or organism that causes disease

pellicle .... thin, firm, yet elastic layer over the cell membrane that gives shape to some microorganisms

penicillin ..._Serendipity_............................ antibiotic formed by Penicillium chrysogenum which, when discovered, opened a whole new world of medicine

peptidoglycan .... large molecules in the bacterial cell wall; molecular basis of the Gram stain

phagocytosis .... process of enclosing food particles by the cell membrane to form an internal food vacuole

phototaxis .... organism's response to the variability of light in its surroundings

phycoerythrin .... red pigment responsible for the color of species of the phylum Rhodophyta; also found in some cyanobacteria

phycology .... study of algae

phylum .... level of taxon below kingdom; also called division in the plant and plant-like kingdoms

Plantae .... kingdom which contains multicellular eukaryotic organisms which are capable of producing their own food, commonly known as plants

plasmodial slime mold .... common name of fungi-like protists which are species of the phylum Myxomycota; characterized by a multi-nucleated feeding structure called a plasmodium

plasmodium (pl. plasmodia) .... multi-nucleated structure of the feeding phase of species of the phylum Myxomycota

prion .... abnormal protein structure which is pathogenic prokaryote .... cellular structure with no true nucleus or any other membrane-bound internal structures

Protista .... kingdom of eukaryotic organisms which do not fit into the kingdoms Animalia, Plantae, or Fungi

protozoan .... common name used for animal-like protists

pseudopodia (sing. pseudopodium) .... cytoplasmic extentions of a cell which are used for motility and phagocytosis

radiolarian .... common name of amoeboid protozoans of the phylum Foraminifera; characterized by tiny shell-like structure composed of silicon

receptor site .... external cell structure on a host cell which allows a virus to recognize and attach to it

red algae .... common name of plant-like protists which are species of the phylum Rhodophyta; mostly composed of multicellular algae with a characteristic red color

red eyespot .... light-sensitive structure in some microorganisms; important for phototaxis

red tide .... algal bloom of a member of the phylum Pyrrophyta (dinoflagellates)

viral replication .... formation of new virions during a viral infection of a host cell

resolving power .... ability to clearly distinguish between two points

rhizoids .... mycelia responsible for obtaining food from the non-living organic matter which a fungus is growing on

Rhizopoda .... phylum of amoeboid protozoans

rickettsia .... group of small eubacteria which are all obligate intracellular parasites

ring .... structure found on some mushrooms around the stalk which is left over from a protective covering that was present when the mushroom was first developing

sac fungi .... common name of species of the phylum Ascomycota; characterized by sac-shaped fruiting bodies

salinity .... concentration of salt in a body of water

saprophytes .... organism which obtains food from non-living organic material

scanning electron microscope .... electron microscope capable of producing three dimensional images

slug phase .... phase in the life cycle of cellular slime mold when the individual cells congregate into a slug-like structure from which fruiting bodies will form

spirillum .... spiral-shaped bacteria

sporangiophore .... stalk-like structure of mycelia which supports the sporangium of species of the phylum Zygomycota

sporangium .... spore-producing structure of species of the phylum Zygomycota

spores .... reproductive cells often covered with a protective coating

staining .... addition of a specific stain to a specimen to enhance the visibility of a specific structure before viewing it under a microscope

stalk .... stem-like structure of a mushroom which supports the cap and gills

stolon .... mycelia of species of the phylum Zygomycota which act as anchors and connect the sporangiophores of a mold structure

sulcus .... groove in the outer covering of species of the phylum Pyrrophyta where a short flagellum is typically found

symbiosis .... mutually beneficial relationship between two species; lichens are an example

taxis .... organism's response to a stimulus

thallus .... body structure of an alga

thermoacidophile .... Archaea which live in high temperature and/or acidic environments

transduction .... sharing of genetic material between bacterium through a bacteriophage

transformation .... sharing of genetic material of bacteria through taking in naked genetic material from the bacterial surrounding

viral attachment protein .... part of the viral capsid protein which will bind with the receptor site on a specific type of host cell

viral budding .... release of virions from the host cell through the cell membrane; this process includes encasing the virion with an envelope composed of lipids from the host cell membrane

virion .... single virus unit; includes the genetic material and a protein capsid

viroid .... disease-causing RNA molecule

virologist .... scientist who studies viruses

virulence .... ability of a virus to cause disease

water mold .... common name of fungi-like protists which are species of the phylum Oomycota. Most species are either plant parasites or found in fresh-water environments

wet-mount .... specimen prepared for viewing on a microscope slide using water or another liquid

Zoomastigophora .... phylum of protozoans with whip-like structures called flagella. Species in this phylum are commonly known as flagellates

Zygomycota .... phylum (or division) of fungi commonly known as mold

zygosporangium .... sexual reproductive structure formed where two hyphae of mold contact each other

zygospore .... reproductive cell containing genetic material from each parent organism; able to grow into a complete new mold structure